Weight Training for All Sports

Weight Training
for All Sports

Howard Payne

PELHAM BOOKS
London

First published in Great Britain by
Pelham Books Ltd, 44 Bedford Square,
London WC1B 3DU
1979
Reprinted 1983

ISBN 0 7207 1124 X

Filmset and printed in Great Britain by BAS Printers
Limited, Over Wallop, Hampshire
and bound by Dorstel Press, Harlow

Contents

Acknowledgments

We would like to say a special thank you to
Pauline Hill, John Horridge, Suresh Joshi,
Lynne Michel, Luigi Pelosi, Maxine Ross,
Makhan Singh, Robert Weir and Mike Wood
for their help with this book.

Picture Credits
The photograph on page 74 is by courtesy of
Powersport International Ltd; all other
photographs are by Howard Payne.

Foreword

by Denis Howell, M.P.,
Minister for Sport, 1974–1979

All sportsmen and sportswomen look for ways of making themselves better at their chosen sports and consult books written about skills and tactics. There is one activity that can benefit nearly all sports by making the players fitter, stronger and more able to exercise their skills. It is cheap, simple, consumes little time, and is even enjoyable – that activity is weight training.

It is only in very recent years that the benefits of a good basic programme of resistance exercises has been recognized, not only as being valuable in itself for general fitness and strength, but also as a great boost to performance in other fields of sport. One aspect of changing attitudes is that weight training is fast losing its unfeminine image and many women are discovering that they can become stronger without acquiring unsightly muscles.

However, when an activity like this does become 'fashionable' there is a danger of youngsters jumping on the bandwagon and rushing into the nearest gymnasium to throw weights about wildly. Weight training is largely unsupervised – in a swimming pool there are lifesavers on duty, and in gym clubs coaches are usually present, but in a weights room there is, in general, no supervision, and there are risks for beginners working alone. These risks are not only in terms of personal safety but also of not exercising properly. Judgment and experience are needed, for which a sensible basis is provided in this book written by athletes with years of personal involvement in sport behind them, and who have both used weights successfully.

This is a book that should be read by those who have only the vaguest notion of what weight training is about, by those who definitely want to try it but do not know how to start, and by those who have experimented with weights but do not clearly understand the principles underlying what they are doing. It will also be useful for teachers and coaches who need a basic illustrated guide to work from when helping others.

Only those who have tried weight training can relish the variety and interest that it can provide. A great deal of beneficial work can be done in a short time, and in bad weather too . . . but the best way to find out is to try it!

Yours in sport,

Denis Howell

Introduction

Sport is concerned with optimum human performance – getting the best out of your body and mind. With normal development and an average liking for physical movement anyone can enjoy most sports up to a certain level. The average casual sportsman or sportswoman will improve this level of participation merely by playing the odd game or swimming or running occasionally because the so-called 'training effect' starts almost immediately you begin a new activity. However, if you are even slightly serious about a sport, you will probably be prepared to indulge in a programme of training which will improve your performance much more effectively than casual participation can do. Usually this training will consist of practising certain movements over and over, preferably with someone watching to tell you whether you are getting it right. For instance a golfer will practise his tee shots by driving a bucketful of balls, one after the other, down a practice fairway, and rugby forwards will improve their line-out actions by trying several line-outs in the training session.

But in addition to the skill-learning involved in these practices you can also improve your performance by exercising to improve the condition, or 'fitness', of your body. For example, if you are a rugby forward you may wish to increase your strength; if you are a squash player you may wish to increase your endurance; if you are a gymnast you may wish to increase your flexibility; and if you are a soccer player you may wish to increase your speed. A beginner at a sport may need to increase all of these qualities. This book is about that particularly successful means of conditioning the human body for sport known generally as weight training.

Now is a good time to dispose of a few fallacies and old wives' tales about weight training:
1. Weight training will not make you 'muscle-bound', whatever that mysterious word means. To obtain muscle development like a Mr Universe, you will have to train extremely hard on special schedules and eat special diets. In any case most body builders who train for Mr Universe contests are good sportsmen, and not at all stiff and inflexible as the word 'muscle-bound' seems to imply.
2. Sensible weight training has never harmed anyone who has observed simple commonsense rules of safety.
3. Women can benefit from weight training, and, contrary to some beliefs, they can make their figures more attractive without becoming hard and lumpy.

The magic of weight training is that it can be all things to all people. Using the appropriate schedules (and sometimes appropriate diets), fat people can become trim, thin people can put on weight, the weak can become strong, the strong can become stronger, the slow can speed up, the

9

breathless-after-one-flight-of-stairs can improve their condition, the ponderous can become dynamic, the convalescent can speed up their recovery, and, most important for readers of this book, it can transform your sporting performance.

There is no denying that weights are of more benefit to some sports than others, for example although no shot putter can hope to get by without them, many international-class tennis players and golfers never touch them. Which is not to say that weight training can't help tennis players and golfers – some international-class performers in these sports swear by weight training and never miss a session – it is just that the skill factor in these sports is of such major importance that some players are reluctant to spend valuable time on conditioning exercises. Even in sports with a strong weight training tradition, such as track athletics, there are the few characters who manage to gain considerable success in spite of the fact that they lift no weights – this is usually because they make up for the lack of weight training by increasing their running mileage. Similarly there are a few swimmers with Olympic medals who shun the weights; however, the majority of top-class swimmers and track and field athletes include some form of weight training in their schedules. Even in those sports with a very high skill content more and more participants are beginning to use weights as they find sheer physical condition becoming a decisive success factor in the demands of modern-day competition at the top levels.

Weight training has one major advantage over other forms of conditioning – it takes less time. Except for throwers and competitive weightlifters who need longer sessions, in our opinion, optimum gains can be made by spending just one hour three times a week in the weights gymnasium. Conditioning of the human body occurs as it adapts itself to demands imposed upon it. Once it has adapted to a certain workload the demand has to be increased for further conditioning to occur. Using weights this progressive increase in the demands of the exercise is very easily effected merely by increasing the poundage being lifted. Motivation is required in any conditioning exercise, and again weights have an advantage over the other methods since you know immediately the results of your efforts, an aspect considered important by psychologists. Also you can almost always see a steady improvement with regular weight training, and as this is easily measured by reference to the amount of weight being lifted, you are further motivated.

Lifting weights has a limitation in that gravity always acts in the vertical direction. But this is only a minor limitation which can be overcome by positioning the body in such a way that, although the weights move against gravity, the load can be directed at any angle relative to the body. Many gymnasiums contain weight training machines which use ropes, chains, pulleys, wheels etc. to allow the resistance to be varied to almost any direction.

Although many modern gymnasiums boast complicated chrome-plated equipment in luxurious surroundings, you can purchase enough basic weights at reasonable prices to start training in your own home. At various times when we have lived far from the nearest gymnasium we have had to train in the kitchen, the spare bedroom, the attic, the garage and even the garden. In one flat we had to cease because the plaster was cracking off the ceiling of the flat below! Be careful also because a keen weight training friend became very unpopular with his wife when, training in their dining-room, he dropped a loaded barbell on to the sideboard filled with best china and crystal.

However there are many advantages in training in a properly equipped gymnasium. As a sports enthusiast you will know the pleasures of meeting people and making friends in your sport. Weight training will increase these opportunities, because in the gymnasium you will meet people from many different sports, each helping the other with their exercises. You will also learn more from training with others and you will be better motivated than if you train alone at home.

At the end of a good weights session you should feel pleasantly tired – but you will also know in your mind that you have made a positive step along the way towards that goal of perfect and optimum functioning of your body in sport. And the next time you participate in your sport you will have that extra confidence – for example your grip will be stronger and more effective in your golf swing, you will find yourself maintaining form even at the end of a long game of tennis, you will be reaching those 'impossible' returns in badminton, you will be up with the ball in soccer and rugby, and generally you will have a new spring in your legs and a new strength in your arm.

Important Note for Beginners

Beginners are advised to read the whole of this book before attempting any of the exercises. It is especially important that you study the sections on safety and the warm-up.

1 The Muscles and the Mind

The Muscles of the Body

There are three types of muscle in the human body:

(a) smooth muscle – found mainly in the internal organs, and which does not concern us in this book;

(b) heart muscle – found only in the heart, and although not subject to voluntary control, it responds to training and its condition and function can be improved;

(c) striated muscle – makes up the muscles attached to the skeleton and is controlled voluntarily.

In order to start an object moving, or to alter its movement once started, a force, or forces, must act. The movements of the human body depend upon the forces of skeletal muscle contraction, with some seven hundred or so different muscles working in groups to provide all the complexity of movement available to us. Under the microscope it can be seen that the muscles of the skeleton consist of long, thin elements called myofibrils, which have alternating light and dark bands giving them a striated, or striped, appearance. Large numbers of myofibrils go to make up muscle fibres, and bundles of these in sheaths of connective tissue make up fasciculi, which in turn are grouped to form a muscle.

The muscle fibres are stimulated to contract by nerve fibres from the spinal cord, a single motor-nerve fibre acting on a so-called motor unit of from one to 150 muscle fibres, which all respond by contracting maximally. This is an all-or-nothing situation with the strength of the total muscle contraction having to depend upon the number of motor units innervated. However, although a muscle fibre is contracting maximally or not at all, the force of its contraction does depend upon the chemical nutrients present. For example, the waste products formed when the muscle fibre is fatigued can lead to a weak contraction.

Muscles consist mainly of water and protein with small amounts of other substances. Energy for contraction of the muscle myofibril is released when the linkage between two types of protein is broken in the chemical change brought about by the motor nerve impulse. There are several different chemical reactions involved in muscle contraction which we won't go into since they are beyond the scope of this book, but it is necessary to point out that there are two processes by which energy is produced for muscle contraction:

(a) Anaerobic activity is that in which oxygen is not required and energy is obtained from chemicals already present in the tissues. This enables the sprinter, for example, to engage in strenuous movements for a short time. Waste products such as lactic acid build up, and

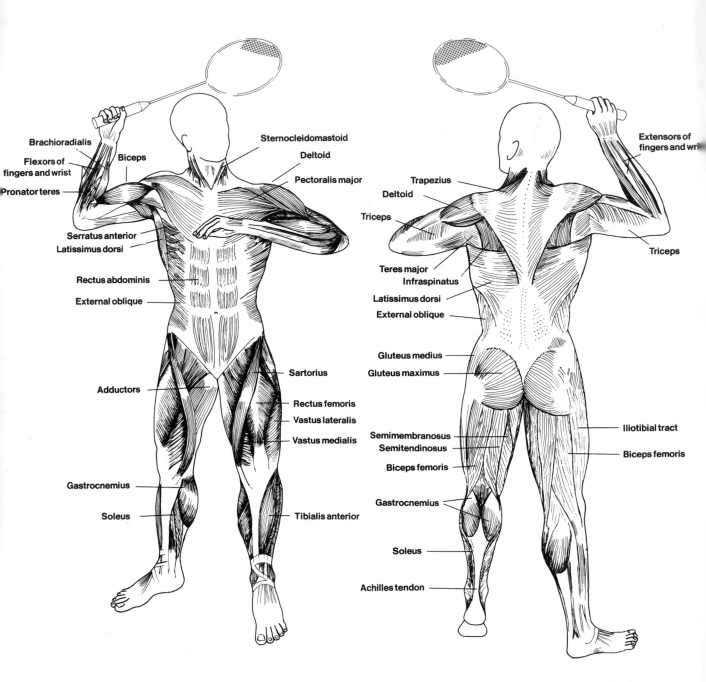

Brachioradialis

Flexors of
fingers and wrist

Pronator teres

Biceps

Sternocleidomastoid

Deltoid

Pectoralis major

Serratus anterior

Latissimus dorsi

Rectus abdominis

External oblique

Adductors

Sartorius

Rectus femoris

Vastus lateralis

Vastus medialis

Gastrocnemius

Soleus

Tibialis anterior

Trapezius

Deltoid

Triceps

Teres major

Infraspinatus

Latissimus dorsi

External oblique

Gluteus medius

Gluteus maximus

Semimembranosus

Semitendinosus

Biceps femoris

Gastrocnemius

Soleus

Achilles tendon

Extensors of
fingers and wri

Triceps

Iliotibial tract

Biceps femoris

1 Diagram of the superficial muscles of the front
of the body.

2 Diagram of the superficial muscles of the back
of the body.

eventually limit the time for which this high-intensity work can last. Oxygen from the air breathed is then needed to remove these waste products before further work can be done, and sports physiologists talk about the 'oxygen debt' caused by anaerobic activity. (b) Aerobic activity is a steady-state situation where the intensity of the movement is low enough for the cardiovascular system to meet the demand for oxygen, and although lactic acid levels may be high they are being kept in check by the oxygen available. A marathon runner will need to function on the aerobic production of energy for over two hours.

Many games require a combination of both these kinds of activity, for example in soccer and rugby short anaerobic bursts are necessary when you have possession of the ball, or are chasing someone else with the ball, but you will probably only require aerobic jogging to keep in position most of the time. Ordinary weight training is an anaerobic activity, since rests are taken between sets of lifts, but special 'circuit'-type schedules can be arranged with lighter poundages for aerobic training.

Anaerobic weight training tends to increase the strength, speed and co-ordination of the muscle contractions, and in certain circumstances will tend to increase the muscle size. Aerobic circuit weight training aids the development of the circulatory-respiratory system. There will always be an overlapping of the benefits obtained from the two types of training, as the circuit trainer will gain a certain amount of strength, and the normal weightlifter will improve slightly his cardiovascular function.

Recent research seems to suggest that there are two, and possibly three types of muscle fibre associated with anaerobic and aerobic work – fast-twitch fibres, which do not depend on oxygen supply for their energy supply, and slow-twitch fibres, which do require oxygen for contraction. The third type supposedly has characteristics of both, and, although fast, also depends on oxygen.

Types of Muscle Contraction

If you attempt to lift a weight which is too heavy for you to budge, you will be contracting muscles which do not shorten once all the slack in the tendons has been taken up. This is an *isometric* contraction, or one in which the muscle stays the same length.

A muscle contraction is said to be *isotonic* when it is contracting, and either shortening concentrically or lengthening eccentrically. I perform an isotonic concentric contraction when I rise from a sitting position, and when I lower myself down gently into a chair I perform an isotonic eccentric contraction.

You may also come across references to so-called *isokinetic* training apparatus, which allows one to exert maximum contraction against a load which nevertheless only moves at a pre-set constant speed.

Muscle Function in a Movement

It is very rare for only a single muscle to be involved in a human movement, and usually a whole group of muscles will act together to move a limb. Probably there will be one muscle which bears the main responsibility for the action, but there may be one or two others contributing to the action at the same time. Later in the movement of the joint other muscles may start to contract to help the action. All the while yet more muscles may be contracting isometrically to stabilize the rest of the body, or even to neutralize the effect of the main contracting muscles on other parts of the body which are not

15

required to move. Thus it can be seen that most weight training exercises will involve many different muscles.

Force of Muscle Contraction

The force a muscle can produce depends on several factors:

1. Each of us is born with a certain quality of muscle which we have inherited from our parents, so basic strength will vary from person to person. However, everyone can improve this by means of weight training.

2. It has been proved that, for any one person, there is a positive correlation between the strength of a muscle and its cross-sectional area. Training will tend to increase both the size and the strength of the muscles involved.

3. In a muscle contraction only a proportion of the motor units (a motor unit is a group of muscle fibres controlled by one motor nerve) will be innervated, and the greater the number of units involved, the greater will be the force of contraction. Training helps to increase the number of motor units which can be called upon at one time to produce a contraction.

4. The strength of a muscle varies according to the amount it has already contracted. Thus a long, relaxed muscle is able to exert more force than when it is shorter and already partly contracted.

5. The load upon which the muscle is acting affects the force which it can exert. If the load is very light it is difficult to build up a large force of contraction since the load will be moved quickly. As the load is increased, however, the force of contraction can be increased. With further increases there comes a point when the muscle just cannot move the load, and an isometric contraction results. Even beyond this point, when the load is

extending the muscle as it tries to contract, the force of the contraction continues for a while to increase with the load. Negative eccentric weight training methods rely on this principle.

6. In points 1–5 above we have looked at the contractile force of a muscle in an isolated idealized condition. But in the actual human body the muscle is attached via non-contractile tissue to bones which form a system of levers. Levers change the effect that the load has upon the muscles and vice versa. Some levers in the human body are such that heavy loads may be moved slowly, some are such that light loads may be moved quickly, and others are designed to operate somewhere between these extremes.

The angles at the joints will also modify the simple principles 1–5. For instance, although maximum muscle force can be exerted when the arms are straight at the elbow in a curl (see Chapter 4), the optimum angle of the pull of the muscles on the bones of the arm is reached when the elbow joint angle is about 90°, and the conditions as far as leverages are concerned, are even better when this angle becomes smaller than 90°.

Points 4, 5 and 6 above further complicate the picture of what goes on when you lift a weight. We have already seen that many muscles are involved in even simple movements. Now it is evident that the forces exerted by each muscle vary according to the state of contraction and the speed of contraction, and that the total force in a muscle also varies according to the angles of the insertions and the angles of the joints as well as the general lever system involved.

Over a period of time during which regular training is carried out the changes described in points 2 and 3 above will also add their share to the difficulties of the physiologists' analysis of the nature and effects of weight training – and we haven't even looked at the psychological aspects yet!

The Psychology of Weight Training

Skill-learning is a branch of psychology which has some significance for the beginner at weight training, because, although most movements are simple, they do require a period of familiarization. The first time you lift a weight you may feel a little awkward because you are not sure how to adjust your balance, the sheer weight of the barbell will feel strange and your movements will be unco-ordinated. You may also feel apprehensive for your own safety and a little shy because of the other people in the gymnasium. Fortunately this early familiarization is a rapid process, and after a few weeks you should have gained a lot of balance, co-ordination and confidence. To aid you through these early stages it is as well to seek help from a coach or even from the regulars in the gymnasium. You will find that weight trainers are a friendly crowd and always ready to help a beginner.

The skill-learning involved in weight training is speeded up if sessions are frequent and regular – three short sessions a week are going to be more beneficial in this respect than only one long one. It is wise to start on very light weights and not to be in a hurry to increase them. Concentrate on perfecting the techniques in these early sessions, since faults are difficult to eradicate later, and may lead to injury when the weights are heavier.

The motivation to train is an important psychological consideration to all sports players. At the beginning the novelty and the rapid gains are sufficient to keep most people interested, but later when the training is

established and the gains are slow in coming, or have reached a sticking point, boredom may set in. If rewards such as selection for a team or acceptance of entry for a competition depend on it, they may stimulate greater training efforts. Lack of interest in training can start a downward spiral of performance, so obviously motivation is very important. Fortunately weight training contains a huge and challenging variety of exercises, schedules, programmes and methods, so it will be a long time before you exhaust all its possibilities.

Psychologists have shown that motivation depends upon knowledge of results. If you can have some information which tells you how you are performing, you are in a much better position than if the results of your exertions are not clear to you. For example, if you are jogging round a running track, or swimming lengths of a pool, you will be better motivated if someone shouts the times of laps or lengths to you. In weight training you know the poundage you are attempting, and you know immediately if you are successful in lifting it. You can also determine very easily what your maximum single lift in an exercise is by attempting heavier and heavier poundages until you fail to perform the lift. You can then keep a check of your progress over the months as your maximum lifts increase with your strength. Even without attempting maximum lifts you will also have the internal information from your body as repetitions on exercises become easier to perform. In weight training there is always this strong motivation to improve and to continue training.

As you become a regular weight trainer you will discover the many facets of the activity that make for enjoyment combined with maximum benefit, but it is useful here to note some tips to aid motivation:

(a) Keep a diary of your training sessions – there is nothing like a look back to previous performances to spur you on to greater efforts.

(b) Vary your schedules to prevent boredom setting in from doing the same old exercises.

(c) Don't test yourself at every session by attempting maximum lifts – this is a quick way of destroying your interest, since you are soon going to run out of improvement from lack of basic training. It is better to set aside one whole session every three or four weeks, and try for maximum single lifts with assistants, or 'catchers', standing by to help you if necessary. With this planned testing you are bound to be well satisfied because you will have the weeks of training in between.

(d) Make training a habit, fix your sessions at regular times, and don't sacrifice these times for other arrangements if you can possibly manage. Think of your training sessions as being as important as meals!

(e) Train intelligently by analysing your results in your main sport. Learn all you can about your own body and work out exercises and schedules that give you optimum benefit in your sport.

2 Before You Begin

The Equipment

The basic equipment which mainly concerns us in this book is the simple barbell, which is a steel bar about 2½ centimetres (1 inch) in diameter by about 2 metres (6½ feet) long, on to which metal discs with central holes are placed. Discs are paired in a range of poundages, and the bar is loaded symmetrically with discs held in place at each end by metal screw 'collars'. The barbell is held and lifted by gripping with each hand the same distance away from the centre of the bar (except in squatting exercises where the bar is supported at the centre and only steadied by the hand grip). A slightly more expensive barbell with a rotating sleeve is preferable when weights become heavier,

since the tendency of the discs to turn in a lift can then be isolated from the wrists by the sleeve. For instance, Olympic weightlifters would be considerably handicapped if they tried to use an ordinary basic training barbell – they use specially constructed bars with ball-bearing swivels to allow the centre of the bar to rotate freely.

After a few months of training with barbells you may want to try more specialized exercises with dumb-bells, which are just very short barbells for lifting in one hand. Some exercises require one dumb-bell, but most call for a dumb-bell in each hand.

A narrow bench, preferably purpose built with supporting stands at one end, used for bench press and other exercises in the prone

3 Barbells and dumb-bells. Before you lift, check that the retaining collars are fastened.

4 A purpose-built bench-pressing bench.

position, and a pair of squat stands (preferably adjustable for height), are essential items of equipment in any weights gymnasium.

A good gymnasium will have a range of barbells and dumb-bells already made up with discs so that there is no need to be continually changing the disc weights on a single bar. The gymnasium will also contain other items of equipment such as benches and boards which can be varied for angle, horizontal chinning bars and parallel bars. There may also be weight training machines, from the simple safety squat rack and leg press machine to complicated and expensive

5 A weight training gymnasium designed by Howard Payne.

6 A range of fixed weights stored in racks means a tidy and safe gymnasium.

pulley, cable and sliding weight mechanisms. Some gymnasiums look like medieval torture chambers with their racks and wheels specially designed to ensure that you suffer evenly throughout the range of the exercise! However it is as well to realize that no amount of fancy equipment is going to be of much use unless it is used sensibly and diligently. In the distant future there may be electric muscle-stimulating machines in which you lie as the electrodes pulse the muscles for you – and already simple versions of these electric muscle stimulators exist, and have been used to strengthen individual muscles – but in the meantime there is no substitute for good hard work on the weights.

7 Layout of a functional weights room.

Weight Training Definitions and Terms

Weight training is concerned with improving the condition of the body in terms of strength, power and endurance, through the use of repetitive movements (or attempted movements in the case of *isometric* exercises) against a resisting load of some kind.

A *weightlifter* is a person whose sport is the competitive lifting of weights where the objective is to perform successfully, according to the rules, a single repetition with maximum poundage. The two main sports are *Olympic weightlifting*, in which the required lifts are the *snatch* and the *clean and jerk*, and *power weightlifting* in which the required lifts are the *dead-lift*, the *squat* and the *bench press*. Both Olympic and power lifting sportsmen use weight training to help them gain strength for their sports.

Weight training physically improves the muscles involved, and the *body builder* exploits this by using weight training methods in such a way that they change the shape of his body, since he strives for certain desired proportions.

In an exercise a weight trainer will perform several *repetitions* of a movement – for example, pushing a barbell from the chest to overhead in the *press* exercise. At the end of a certain number, or *set*, of repetitions he will stop and rest for a few minutes. The group, or *schedule*, of different exercises the weight trainer performs during that session may include several sets of each exercise. In order to exercise many different muscle groups, or to vary the benefits according to the demands of the weight trainer's sport, he or she will also probably alter the schedule from session to session in a *programme* of weight training lasting several weeks or months (note that the word 'schedule' is sometimes loosely used to include the idea of a 'programme' as well).

Safety and Commonsense Rules for Weight Training

Since weight training is a fairly strenuous activity involving the handling of heavy lumps of ironware when you will be feeling the effects of increasing fatigue, it is wise to obey certain commonsense rules for the safety of yourself and other users of the gymnasium:

1. Don't train on weights when you are ill. Some sportsmen and sportswomen become so obsessed by their training that they will even soldier on with a bad cold or other illness, but at the very least this practice slows down their recovery. When convalescing after an illness it is best to reduce poundages and schedules considerably and to work back to normal very slowly, since this is a notoriously bad time for injuries to occur.

Medical evidence suggests that there is no danger in participating in heavy training during menstruation, but sportswomen who suffer particularly from premenstrual tension and severe first day bleeding may prefer to do only a very light session on these days.

2. Lift weights on a relatively empty stomach. There will be large demands on your blood circulatory system when you are training, so it is not a good idea to have your body digesting a meal at the same time.

3. Wear suitable clothing when training, so that movement is not restricted. Always wear non-slip shoes, and never train in bare feet.

4. Warm up before starting the session.

5. Check before each exercise that the weights you are lifting are secure, and that the metal 'collars' holding the discs in place on the bar are well tightened. Be especially vigilant with dumb-bells, since they are

8 A strong, safe position for starting a lift.

usually swung away from the horizontal when they are lifted.

6. Wherever possible keep the entire surfaces of both feet in contact with the floor when performing an exercise because this provides good balance. For this reason we advise against using the 'step up' exercise, in which

the lifter carries a barbell across the shoulders and steps up and down on a bench, since the balance is precarious for most of the lift.

7. When starting a lift with the weight on the floor, maintain a straight, near-vertical back and lift with the legs. In other words don't attempt derrick-like lifts in which the legs are

straight and the main load is placed on the muscles of the back. The spine is made up of many separate bones and discs which can support quite heavy forces along its length, but you don't need to be a mechanical engineer to appreciate the fact that it should not be subjected to large forces which are angled away from the column.

The exercises in this book will give the back muscles plenty to do without endangering the vertebral column, and we are of the opinion that exercises like the 'good morning' lift, in which a barbell is held across the shoulders and the body is bent forward at the hips until the trunk is at 90° to the straight legs, are potentially dangerous and therefore not recommended.

8. Where there is any danger of your weight inadvertently falling on to others exercising in the vicinity, wait until they have finished and have moved to a position of safety before you start. Similarly be on your guard that you are not in danger from anyone else's exercise.

9. Replace your weights in the racks immediately after the exercise, since a cluttered floor is potentially hazardous.

10. A good maxim to remember is: 'Train, don't strain!' Be careful when attempting to lift a weight heavier than your previous best. In particular, make sure that catchers are standing by when you are handling heavy poundages on the squat and the bench press exercises. Remember that although the first few repetitions may be easy, the weight will become harder to move as you tire.

11. Behave sensibly in the gymnasium, and don't indulge in horseplay.

12. If you have observed the above rules you should never get into difficulties with weights – however if the unlikely does happen and you find yourself falling with a heavy weight, get rid of it quickly by pushing it away from you, and don't attempt to struggle with it.

Weight training exercises and schedules need to be performed intelligently to obtain maximum benefits – the same commonsense should be extended to the simple disciplines necessary to ensure that no accidents or injuries occur in the gymnasium. After all, you are training to *improve* your physical condition!

3 Principles and Methods

Progressive Overload

Lifting weights in an exercise places a certain amount of stress on the human body, and if this same stress occurs regularly as it does in a weight trainer's programme lasting several weeks or months, the body will gradually adapt itself to reduce the stress. In other words the muscles involved will hypertrophy (increase in size) and become stronger and the exercise will feel easier. The whole process can now be repeated by increasing the weight and once more placing a stress on the body. In an actual programme of training, careful timing of small increases in poundages will ensure that the stress is maintained at a level with which the body can cope adequately without excessive fatigue or injury. This adaptation of the body in weight training to gradually increasing weights is known as the progressive overload or progressive resistance principle. The body will adapt very quickly for the beginner, but of course improvement will slow down and eventually stop for someone who trains for many years. It takes a very long time to reach such a state, but even then it is worth continuing with training to maintain one's strength level, since the body will slowly begin to adapt to the state of no stress if training is stopped – that is, the muscles will atrophy (decrease in size) and strength will decline.

Although some recent research has shown that under extreme conditions muscle fibres can split and so increase in number in a muscle, it is thought that, in general, the number of fibres in a muscle is fixed, and that strength is improved by increasing the size of the individual fibres. An additional reason for strength gain through exercise may be that, since muscle action is a function of the central nervous system, depending upon the summation of many nervous impulses to the motor units, there is also a training effect which allows the more effective combined firing of the motor units, causing a stronger contraction in the muscle. This explanation does seem to be borne out by the fact that considerable gain in strength can occur without any appreciable apparent outward increase in size of the muscle. This training effect of increased firing of the motor units seems to be a strong justification for the progressive overload principle, since if you merely plug away at the same old poundage on an exercise the central nervous system will soon settle down to a pattern of firing just those motor units necessary to shift that weight. And this brings us to an important consideration in any weight training programme – it is essential to train intelligently and with a sensible mixture of determination and patience. Determination and willpower are needed to keep the muscles working at maximum capacity and patience is needed to wait for improvement, and not to push on so fast that injury occurs. The word 'overload' should be interpreted with caution.

Specificity of Weights Exercises

Research has shown that the human body adapts specifically to the stress imposed upon it. In the weight training press-to-overhead exercise, for instance, the body will tend to adapt itself so that only those muscles involved in the exercise will strengthen, and they will tend to develop mostly in a way that strengthens them to press a weight to overhead. Shot putters find that the press is not an entirely satisfactory method of producing arm strength for the putting action. The reason for this is because the arm action in shot putting pushes the shot away from the neck at an angle of about 40° to the horizontal, whereas the press moves the weight in a vertical line. So a modified press is required in the weights gymnasium to develop the shoulder and arm muscles for a 40° push – either a Neider press, which pushes the barbell up at that angle, or an incline bench press can be used.

The specific nature of training also means that for overall strength, involving most of the muscles, many different exercises must be used. Some people maintain that specificity extends even to the speed at which the weight is moved, and advise that if the sport calls for a fast movement, the training exercise must also be fast. They go further and suggest that if you train at an exercise exclusively on sets of, say, twenty repetitions, you develop mainly in a way that will benefit you at performing a twenty-repetition set, and although this training will be of some benefit to you when performing a three-repetition set on the same exercise with a

heavier weight, it would have been better if you had trained for this on three repetition sets. This is after all quite logical, since a sprinter trains mainly at sprinting, and a long distance runner needs to train by running long distances (even if they are broken up with short rests as in interval training).

So it is clear that if general conditioning is required, not only must there be a variety of exercises in the schedule, but within each exercise there must also be a variety of repetitions in sets, a variety of speed of movement, and, following on from these, a variety of poundages. And it is also evident that if there is a certain weakness in a part of the body which is detrimental to your sport, you should attempt to devise exercises and schedules which work that part of your body specifically for that sport.

How Often and How Much?

Competitive lifters and body builders need to train five or six days a week on weights, but people using weights to aid conditioning for other sports usually find that two to four sessions a week are all they can manage if they are to train at the sport itself as well. It is possible to get by with just one session a week but not much improvement can be expected, unless a lot of other conditioning and training is taking place during the rest of the week. For example, some long distance runners and swimmers obtain a useful break from their mileage training by spending one session each week in the weights gymnasium. The beginner at weights is advised to have two or three workouts per week which are spaced out so as to allow at least forty-eight hours between sessions.

Most observers agree that the specific nature of weight training is such that low repetitions of, say, one to four with heavy poundages around 90% of a single repetition maximum give optimum strength gains, and high repetitions of eight to twelve or more with light weights of around 70% of a single repetition maximum give optimum muscular endurance gains. Gains of both kinds can be made in the middle range of four to eight repetitions with intermediate poundages.

A beginner's schedule of the type suggested later in this book will take about twenty to thirty minutes to complete, but the more advanced weight trainer may find that not only is he able to include more exercises but that the heavier work requires more rest between sets, so that a session will last up to one and a half hours. Olympic weightlifters and body builders may spend even more time than this at each session in the gymnasium, but their schedules will not be discussed here, since we are concerned with weight training as conditioning for other sports.

The Pyramid System

An ingenious method of combining the benefits of both low-repetition heavy-weight and high-repetition low-weight training is that of the pyramid system. In a particular exercise a series of sets is performed in which the poundage is increased while the number of repetitions per set is reduced. An example will make the method clearer. If in the bench press a lifter can manage, say, 50 kg in a single repetition maximum, his pyramid may take the form of:

    25 kg in a set of ten repetitions, rest, then
    30 kg in a set of eight repetitions, rest, then
    35 kg in a set of six repetitions, rest, then
    40 kg in a set of four repetitions, rest, then
    ending with 45 kg in a set of two repetitions.

Many other variations are possible with this particular example, and the lifter may decide to start at 35 kg and move upwards in only 2½ kg increments, or, if the exercise is an important core to his schedule, he may decide to do seven sets with eight repetitions, seven repetitions, six repetitions, four repetitions etc., and if you are a discus thrower seeking mainly strength you may start even heavier and work through two or three sets each of five repetitions, four repetitions, three repetitions etc.

We think that a pyramid with increasing weights is preferable, since the warming up effect of the early, lighter poundages is important to avoid possible muscle injury, but some weight training methods use an inverted pyramid, starting with the low-repetition high-weight set first. The idea behind this method is that the heavy weights can be used when the muscles are fresh and not fatigued.

In the example given above, the last set is of two repetitions, which is deliberate to avoid the possibility of having to struggle with a single repetition at the lifter's maximum, especially after all the previous sets. Once every three or four weeks, the lifter, after a suitable warm-up, can test again his single repetition best, and if this has improved by, say 5 kg he can at his next session raise each set by 5 kg (in the example, therefore, he will start at 30 kg in a set of ten repetitions).

The pyramid system is not applicable to all weight training exercises, so some discretion is necessary in its use. It is well suited to such exercises as the bench press, the front press and the clean, for example, but it is not recommended for incline board abdominal raises in which muscular endurance is the aim, or for standing curls where increasing weight changes the technique of the lift. In certain exercises like the squat it should be used only if a safety rack is available, since failure to complete a heavy squat in a free position can be dangerous.

The Super Set System

Body builders sometimes follow one exercise immediately by another which involves the antagonist muscles of the first as the prime movers. They will, for example, perform a set of triceps press straight after a curl exercise without resting in between. The first exercise is a warm-up for the second, and ensures a good blood supply to the muscles. However this is also a useful way for the busy sports player to save time, since a rest period can be omitted. It is possible to take this a stage further and include three or four exercises in rotation without rest, provided that one exercise does not cause fatigue in a manner that will affect the others excessively. A useful combination may be, for instance, the bench press, the squat and the side bend. You can then almost immediately repeat the sequence of exercises since the muscles involved in, say, the bench press will have recovered while you were doing the others. Note that this is a time-saving method only and should not be confused with the normal circuit training system, where the purpose is to maintain a high level of endurance stress.

4 The Exercises

Safety Before attempting any of the lifts described in this chapter, read the section on safety in Chapter 2.

Warm-up Always go through a short warm-up routine at the start of a training session. (See Chapter 5).

Breathing Weight training is a strenuous activity in which deep breathing is important to keep the hard working musculature well supplied with oxygen. In some exercises the inhalations can be timed with an extension of the trunk or shoulders, and the exhalations with an inward movement of these parts. However, in most lifts it is better to take a deep breath before the main effort and release it at the top or end of the lift. Huff and puff as much as you can between repetitions – it is the accepted thing to do in weights gymnasiums!

In certain circumstances when holding the breath in heavy exercise dizziness can result from a reduction in blood supply to the brain. A good warm-up will generally prevent this from happening, but if you do feel dizzy, put the weight down immediately.

Barbell Exercises

The Clean This exercise owes its name to the Olympic sport of weightlifting, where it is part of one of the required lifts, the clean and jerk. In the training movement, the barbell is lifted from the floor to the chest where it is held for a second or two, then returned to the floor. As so many other weight training exercises start from an erect standing position and therefore require the barbell to be cleaned to the chest, the clean will be described in detail.

Stand relaxed at the centre of the barbell, so that your feet, comfortably spread about 20 cm apart, are under it and your shins are almost touching it. With your hands at shoulder-width apart, simply bend your knees until your hands can grip the bar, all the while keeping your back as straight and as near vertical as possible, your head high, looking straight ahead, and your heels still in contact with the floor. A firm overgrip should be used, each hand equidistant from the bar centre, and your arms should be straight from relaxed shoulders so that a gentle tension is created on the bar. This starting position for the lift is most important if large weights are to be moved efficiently and without injury. The first part of the lift is now a strong upward drive with your legs while the rest of your body remains as straight and near vertical as possible. When your legs are straight a well timed pull with your arms, while keeping the bar close to your body, will continue, and even add to, the momentum of the barbell. By the time the bar reaches a position about mid-trunk level, the momentum of the bar is sufficient to allow time to dip your body

9 The power clean.   9a   9b

9c

slightly and to swing your elbows under and in front of the bar, so that the bar comes to rest across your chest. With correct timing and balance, the exercise is a most satisfying movement, which makes use of a large number of muscle groups.

The main faults to avoid are:
(a) back lifting if your legs have straightened before the barbell has moved from the floor;
(b) forward movement of the barbell away from your body and/or backward movement of your hips away from the barbell; and
(c) early bending of your arms before your legs have completed their drive.

Returning the barbell to the floor is best achieved by swinging your elbows from under the bar, and allowing the weight to drop on to your thighs. From there it is gently lowered to the floor by bending your knees and keeping your back straight. Always use your legs for lifting or lowering the weight.

Variations
1. *The power clean* as described above involves very little dipping under the bar to receive the weight across the chest.

2. *The squat clean* is used in Olympic weightlifting, where considerable skill is required to exaggerate the dip under the bar so that it is received at the chest in a full squatting position (photograph 10f).

10a–m The Olympic clean and jerk using a squat cleaning technique.

10a

10b

10c

10d

10e

Sequence continues overleaf

10j

10f

10k

10g

11a

11b

11c

11d

11 The split clean.

3. *The split clean* is used by some Olympic weightlifters. The body is dipped fairly low under the bar by bringing one leg forward and bending the other until the knee almost touches the floor.

Beginners should use the power clean and not attempt the others until they have several months of weight training behind them. The Olympic-type cleans are not recommended anyway except for sports requiring

34

exceptional strength, such as the athletic throws.

The Jerk (photographs 10h to 10m) This is the second part of the Olympic lift called the clean and jerk. It is a movement which demands much skill since a very heavy weight has to be lifted to arms' length overhead.

At the end of the clean your elbows should be well up and pushed forward so that the barbell is supported on your chest and shoulders and not just by your arms. The initial bar momentum is gained by a quick bending and straightening of your knees followed by a strong upward arm push. While the bar is still moving upwards at the end of this thrust, dip your whole body under the bar by splitting your legs, and lock your arms straight overhead. You can now stand upright by bringing your feet to a position side by side slightly apart.

Once the timing of the movement has been mastered, the jerk can be included in any schedule designed for strength-with-speed, though repetitions should be restricted to three or four to ensure that good technique is maintained.

The Power Snatch The snatch starting position is the same as in the clean except that the hands are much further apart. In Olympic snatching the hands are very wide so that the weight only has to be lifted just above the head to comply with the rule that the bar must be lifted from the floor to full arm's length above the head in one movement. In the weight training exercise it is not necessary to spread the hands quite so far apart, but the movement is more effective if the grip is wider than in the clean.

The barbell is lifted in a smooth quick action which keeps it close to your body until it is overhead, when a slight dip of your body and a rotation of your wrists completes the lift to bring the weight to arm's length

12a–d The power snatch.

12a

12b

Sequence continues overleaf

12c

12d

overhead. This is called a power snatch, since there is very little dipping under the bar at the end. The Olympic snatch requires a pronounced dip under the bar bringing the

lifter into a full squatting position with the bar overhead, before he stands up – but this is a highly skilled movement and is not recommended here for weight training.

13 The Olympic snatch using the squat technique.

13a

13b

Variations

1. *The split snatch* is also a movement requiring a lot of skill learning, which is used by some Olympic weightlifters. However it does not call for the delicate balance and split-second timing of the squat snatch, and since it is an excellent all-round exercise, many weight trainers include it in their schedules.

The first part of the lift is the same as the power snatch, but as the bar reaches chest height dip your body very low under the bar by thrusting one leg forward and bending the other until the knee almost touches the floor. At the same time your wrists are rotated and the arms locked out overhead. From this deep split position the lifter stands up before lowering the weight to the floor. Used as a weight training exercise it is even better if the actions of the legs are reversed in each repetition, so that both legs are worked equally.

14 Part of the split snatch.

13c

13d

15 The front press.

2. Both the power and the split snatches can be performed from a *hang position* instead of from the floor by starting the pull, in the second and subsequent repetitions, before the weight actually touches the floor. This makes for a more energetic exercise with a sharper pull.

Although poundages will be small at first, and the learning of the skills takes some time, the various types of snatch are most rewarding both in terms of general body conditioning and in the sense of satisfaction to be obtained from well timed lifts.

The Press The front press is started from a standing position after the barbell has been cleaned to the chest. With the bodyweight well forward on to the balls of your feet, heels still on the floor, the barbell is pushed straight upwards to arm's length. An overgrip with hands a few centimetres further apart than in the clean exercise is used.

Variations
1. *The front press,* as described above.
2. *The front push press* incorporates a preliminary knee bend followed by a fast straightening and this allows heavier weights to be used, since the extra initial momentum carries the barbell through the early 'sticking' points.
3. *The press behind the neck* starts with the bar resting across your shoulders and the top of your back and requires a slightly different balance with your head forward, so that the bar doesn't strike the back of your head on the way up or down. Less weight on the bar is possible, but this exercise is good for shoulder mobility.

16a

16 The press behind the neck.

16b

16c

17a

17b

17 The seated front press.

4. *The seated press in front* places more emphasis on sheer strength because aiding movements of the lower body are prevented.
5. *The seated press behind the neck* is also used to immobilize the lower body.

   In seated presses use very light poundages,

or make sure that an assistant is standing by.

Pressing of all kinds strengthens mainly the muscles of the shoulder region, but many other muscle groups are also involved in the standing presses.

18 The seated press behind the neck.

18a

18b

The Curl An undergrip is used for the curl, with your hands fairly close together to allow your forearms to remain parallel throughout. The starting position is with the body standing erect, the arms straight and the bar resting against the thighs. From here the bar is 'curled' upwards to the chin, the elbows staying close to the sides of the body.

19 The curl.

19a

19b

19c

Variations

1. *The reverse curl* is as described above for the normal curl except that an overgrip is used.

2. Body building curling exercises make use of special apparatus. For example 'preacher curls' are performed with the upper arms supported on a stand, and angled hand positions are made possible with bars that are made in a zig-zag shape.

Curling exercises mainly the muscles of the arms. As these muscles are well used in many other exercises curls can be omitted from general conditioning schedules if time is short. On the other hand curls are particularly useful in specific arm strengthening where it is required to restrict the movement to the arms only.

The Squat *(Deep Knee Bend)* The squat is performed by doing a knee bend with the barbell supported on the shoulders behind the neck. Beginners may get to the starting position by cleaning the weight to the chest, pressing it above the head and bringing it down behind the neck, but after a few weeks of normal progress the weight will be too heavy for this method and squat stands, or assistants, will be required. Since the squat uses the very strong muscles of the legs and lower trunk, heavier weights than in most other exercises are necessary to work these muscles sufficiently. Good technique and safety should be uppermost in the lifter's mind, because the lower back and the knees are especially vulnerable if certain positions of leverage are adopted.

Some people place a folded towel or track suit between the bar and the shoulders, but a little perseverance will accustom you to having the bar in direct contact across a wide expanse of shoulders, neck and back with the hands well spread apart . The practice of raising the heels with a plank of wood to ease tight Achilles tendons is also to be avoided, if possible, since the mobility will only come if the tendons are stretched regularly by squatting with the heels firmly on the floor, even if at first only partial squats can be performed under these conditions.

20 The reverse curl.

20a

20b

21a

21b

21 The squat.

The starting position is with the body erect, very slightly forward so as to balance the weight evenly on feet which are comfortably spread about 20 cm apart. The movement into the full squatting deep knee bend is controlled all the way downwards so that there is no 'bouncing' or sudden change of direction at the bottom of the lift. The knees should go forward over the toes, not inwards or sideways. All the while your back should be kept straight, the eyes looking forward, with only a slight bending forward at your hips. The return upwards to the standing position should also use the same back and head posture, the work being done mainly with the legs. As mentioned before, the heels must be kept on the floor at all times, since the high combined centre of gravity of lifter and barbell produces a precarious balance if there is a shift forwards on to the toes. Squat only as low as you can with your heels down.

21c

22a

22b

22 The half squat in a safety rack.

Remember too the other safety rules when squatting and don't be tempted to use poundages which are too heavy for you – if in doubt make sure that catchers are standing by.

Performed correctly, the squat is a satisfying and highly beneficial exercise for almost every sport.

Variations

1. *The half-squat* has a lowest position when the thighs are at about 45°, so even heavier weights may be used. However, the heavier weights make it imperative that safety racks are used or that catchers are at hand. The quarter squat is more restrictive still, and should only be used in a highly specialized schedule.

2. *Jump squats* are more vigorous in the upward movement than normal squats, and the extra momentum carries the lifter into the air in a low vertical jump. For obvious reasons we do not recommend this lift with its airborne phase while heavy weights are carried high on the shoulders. If used at all it should be by experienced field event athletes. In any case there is an excellent alternative in the vertical jump with dumb-bells (described in the section on exercises with dumb-bells).

3. *Front squats* are very good for emphasizing a slightly different balance from the normal squat, but the lift is rather uncomfortable! A much lighter barbell is held in front across your chest and shoulders as in the starting position for the front press, except that it is

44

helpful to push your elbows even higher and further forward. The deep knee bend is now performed with a very upright trunk. Remember to keep your heels on the floor, and don't go any lower than the position where your heels tend to rise.

Bench Press Skill plays a smaller part in the bench press than in many other lifts and partly for this reason it is satisfying as a movement you can 'get your teeth into'. The chest, arm, shoulder and back muscles involved are particularly susceptible to improvement through this exercise, which helps to make it a great favourite amongst weight trainers.

The lifter lies on a sturdy narrow bench with a leg on each side of the bench and feet firmly in contact with the floor to prevent any sideways movement. If a stand for the barbell is used this should be adjusted so that it is in a position above your face and at a height which is almost at full arm's stretch. For good visibility when returning the barbell to the stands the supports should be closer together than the handgrip. This overgrasp grip is very wide, so that the forearms are parallel and vertical when the bar reaches its lowest point across the chest. If no stand is available, a single assistant is best if the weight is not too heavy for him. He should hand the barbell to the lifter so that an evenly spaced grip is

23 The front squat.

23a

23b

24a

24b

24c

possible on either side of the assistant's grip. If two assistants are helping with the weight, it is essential for balance that they both release or recover the barbell at the same time on a signal from the lifter.

The starting position for the lift is with the barbell at full arm's length directly above the chest, and the lift consists of a fast but controlled lowering of the weight until the bar touches the chest, followed by a vigorous push back to the starting position.

Variations

1. *The narrow grip bench press* is a specialized exercise which requires a shoulder-width or narrower grip.

2. *The incline bench press* changes the angle of the movement relative to the general body

24 The bench press.

25 The incline bench press.

25a

25b

26a 26b

26 The decline bench press.

position, and most incline benches can be set to several different angles. Make sure that the feet are firmly anchored, so that there is no danger of slipping. You should realize that less poundage can be handled than in the normal bench press.

3. *The decline bench press* allows the head to be lower than the trunk. A narrower grip is usual, but, as in the incline press, make sure that the feet are well secured.

Bent-over Rowing Exercise This exercise is, in effect, the reverse of the bench press, the weight being pulled upwards to your chest while your trunk and head are facing the floor

in a forward bent-over position. Your legs, straight at the knees, are spread giraffe-fashion further apart than in most other standing exercises since this makes it easier to lean forward until your trunk is parallel to the ground. While in this posture the barbell, held in a wide grip, is pulled from arm's length to touch the chest in a movement which is specific in exercising the muscles of the back and arms.

Variations

1. The bent-over rowing exercise can be varied to bring in slightly different muscles by *pulling to the waist* or *to the neck* instead of the chest.

27 The bent-over rowing exercise.

27a 27b

28a

28b

28 Upright rowing.

2. *The upright rowing motion* differs so much from the bent-over version that it hardly qualifies as a variation. It is nonetheless an excellent exercise for the muscles around the shoulders. A very narrow overgrasp grip is used with your hands almost touching, and, as the name suggests, your body is in the erect standing posture. Your elbows remain above the bar as it is pulled from a position

against your thighs until it touches your chin.
3. Variations of the bent-over rowing movement can be performed *with special benches* and *inclined boards* if they are constructed so as to allow free movement of the barbell underneath. The lifter lies face downwards on the bench or board, arms hanging down on either side, and performs the rowing action by pulling the barbell up

29 The bent arm pull-over.

29a

29b

towards the chest.

The Bent Arm Pull-over This is an exercise that can be used either for general strengthening of the muscles of the chest and upper arm, or purely as a breathing help after heavy lifting on squats, for example. It is performed lying on a bench as in the bench press, except that your head is allowed to hang over the end of the bench to aid full expansion of your lungs. An overgrip is used with your hands shoulder-width apart. The exercise starts with the bar resting on your chest, and without straightening your arms at the elbows, the weight is carried over your head and lowered below the bench until your chest and shoulders are fully stretched. During this movement up, over and beyond your head, a continuous breath is inhaled until the lungs are fully inflated at the end, stretched position. A long slow exhalation accompanies the pull back to the starting position, your elbows remaining bent throughout. Used as a breathing exercise the lift can be performed fifteen to twenty times with an unloaded bar.

Variation

The straight arm pull-over may be used in a similar manner to the bent arm pull-over, though the more difficult leverage involved restricts it to smaller poundages. The general movement is the same except that the elbows are kept straight throughout, and the starting position is either with the bar resting on your thighs, or directly overhead as in the bench press. The bent arm pull-over is recommended as being more efficient.

The High Pull This movement is identical to the clean, except that the final dip under the bar is omitted, and the weight is lowered again to the ground. This means that more

30a

30b

30 The straight arm pull-over.

49

31a

31 The high pull.

weight can be loaded on the bar, and that more effort can be put into the pull from the floor, since there is no distraction from a need to time a dip under the bar. However this lift, with its lack of conclusion, is not as satisfying as the clean, although you may gain incentive for the mental effort required, by considering it an assistance exercise for the clean!
Variation
The snatch high pull is, again, similar to the normal power snatch except that the bar is not finally taken to arm's length overhead – the extra weighted bar is pulled as high as possible (probably to about mid-trunk height) and then lowered again to the ground.

The Dead Lift This is a lift which involves the strongest muscles of the body, and as it calls for the heaviest poundages of any of the weight training exercises, it should not be used in a beginner's schedule. It simply

31b

31c

32a

32b

32 The dead lift.

consists of holding the barbell with straight arms and standing upright, the top of the lift being a standing position with the bar resting against the thighs. In order to prevent the very heavy weight from slipping from your grasp, an alternate grip is used, one hand in overgrip and the other in undergrip, with your hands about shoulder-width apart. Although the lift is simple, it is essential that all the work is done with your legs, while the back remains straight and almost vertical. A derrick-type lift by your back with your legs straight is potentially dangerous for the lower spine, and anyway your back muscles will have plenty to do even when the lift is performed correctly. Remember to lower the weight the same way – with your legs.

33 Leather or canvas straps wound around the wrists and the bar may be used to aid the grip in heavy high pulling and dead lifting.

34 The astride dead lift.

Variations

1. *The astride dead lift* is very much like the normal dead lift, but you straddle the bar with a leg on either side and grasp the bar with an alternate grip with one hand in front, and the other behind your back. In standing up the barbell will come up between your legs.

2. *The hack dead lift* varies the angle of the body pull on the bar and tends to ensure safe leg lifting. Stand with your back to the bar and squat down to grasp it behind your legs. The movement is an awkward one with the bodyweight further forward and the bar coming upwards against your legs, so start with the weight very much lighter than in the front dead lift.

Calf Muscle Exercises The calf muscles normally get plenty of exercise from the general activities in the gymnasium, and when running about in sport, and, as every body builder knows, these muscles are notoriously difficult to build up through specific weight training.

35 The hack dead lift.

36a

36b

36 The upright calf raise.

If you can bear a really heavy weight across your shoulders, you can try the *upright calf raise* by simply raising yourself up on your toes and then lowering your heels again. This has to be done in a safety rack of some kind, and can also be more effective if done with the toes on the edge of a 5 cm thick plank of wood, so that the full ankle range is used.

You can get almost the same benefit without weights from keeping your own bodyweight directly over your toes by holding on to something rigid like a door post, table or heavy chair. When the exercise becomes too easy with two legs, stand on one leg at a time.

Seated calf raises can also be tried, but require very heavy weights to be effective. The extension of the ankles is performed with the toes on the edge of a 5 cm thick plank of wood while supporting a barbell across the lower thighs in the seated position.

Probably the best way of exercising the calf muscles is to run repetition short distances on the toes.

37 The seated calf raise.

37a

37b

Dumb-bell Exercises

The weighted barbell has many advantages – it can be loaded to any poundage capable of being lifted by the human body, the weight can be kept very close to the body throughout a lift, and movement of the arms relative to each other is prevented. The last advantage can also be a disadvantage, though, since many supporting muscle groups are made redundant and not exercised. Balancing the barbell is difficult in single arm lifts, and its large moment of inertia means that it cannot easily be swung away from the horizontal.

The dumb-bell, which is really just a very short barbell, is ideal for single or independent arm lifts. Remember that the weight can move in any direction and so will feel very different from the two hand barbell lift, so start with low poundages. Also always check that the collars on your dumb-bells are secure – loose dumb-bell collars are the cause of many accidents. When lifting dumb-bells from the floor, stand as close to them as possible, and lift with the legs keeping the back straight and almost vertical. In cleaning dumb-bells to the shoulders let your hands turn inwards slightly from the normal barbell overgrip position. Recognize that the support at the shoulders will be more difficult than with a barbell.

38 Keep your back straight and lift with your legs.

39a

39b

39 The dumb-bell press.

Dumb-bell Press Although you can perform single arm dumb-bell presses with only one dumb-bell at a time, it is more usual to work with a dumb-bell in each hand and press them simultaneously.

Variation
The alternate dumb-bell press requires a dumb-bell in each hand, and as one is pressed upwards, the other is lowered. The exercise is easier than the simultaneous press so slightly heavier weights can be used.

40 The alternate dumb-bell press.

40a

40b

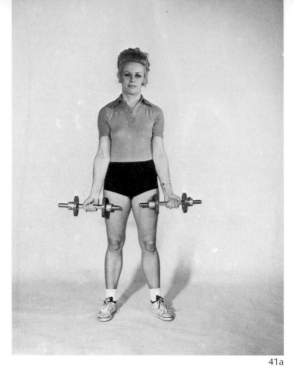

41a

41b

41 The dumb-bell curl.

Dumb-bell Curls Body builders prefer the dumb-bell curl to the straight barbell curl since the former allows the position of the hand to be turned to any angle so that the muscles concerned can be worked completely.

Variation

A variation which attempts to work the muscles through the whole range of hand angles possible is the *alternating rotating dumb-bell curl*. The arms alternate, one flexing while the other extends. At the same time each arm performs a rotating type of movement, starting the curl with a normal undergrip, gradually turning over as the lift progresses until it becomes an overgrip at full contraction. The weight is lowered slowly with the overgrip and near the full extension the rotation of the hand is reversed to bring it back into the undergrip position for the start of the next lift.

42 The alternating rotating dumb-bell curl.

42a

42b

42c

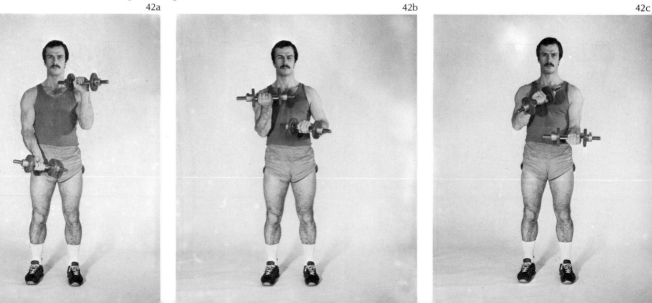

43a

43b

43 The bench press with dumb-bells.

Bench Press with Dumb-bells Unless the weights are very light an assistant should give and receive one of the dumb-bells at the start and the finish of the set. Because the weights are free to move in any direction, it is particularly important for your own safety that you work well within your capabilities in this exercise.

Variations
1. *The 'flying' exercise* with bent elbows is performed in a similar position, except that the elbows are turned outwards to move wide of the body, and the hands are turned inwards so that the bars are almost parallel.
2. *The 'flying' exercise with straight arms* is also similar, but the elbows are kept straight throughout so the dumb-bells move in a wide arc.

44 The 'flying' exercise.

44a

44b

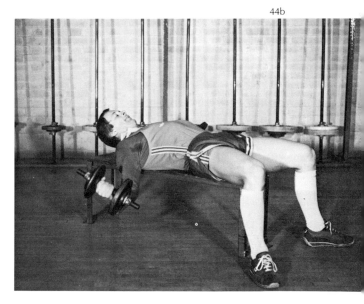

45a

45b

45 Rowing motion with a dumb-bell.

Rowing Motion with a Dumb-bell A dumb-bell may be used in each hand to perform the bent-over rowing exercise, but there is very little or no advantage to be gained over the same exercise with a barbell. The one hand dumb-bell rowing exercise, however, does afford specific advantages for some sports, for example, canoeing. The movement is carried out by bending over as in the barbell exercise, leaning with the free hand on a bench and lifting through an exaggerated range so that the dumb-bell is lifted high past the side of the body.

Step-up on Bench with Dumb-bells Although we don't recommend the step-up exercise for reasons of safety, if it is used at all in a schedule, it is much preferable to carry a dumb-bell in each hand than to balance a barbell on the shoulders. Step up on to a low stable bench, leading with each foot in turn, and making sure that there is full extension of your knees on the bench.

Vertical Jumps with Dumb-bells This is an excellent conditioner for legs and back and is also suitable for endurance work with high

58

Opposite 46 Step-up on bench with dumb-bells.

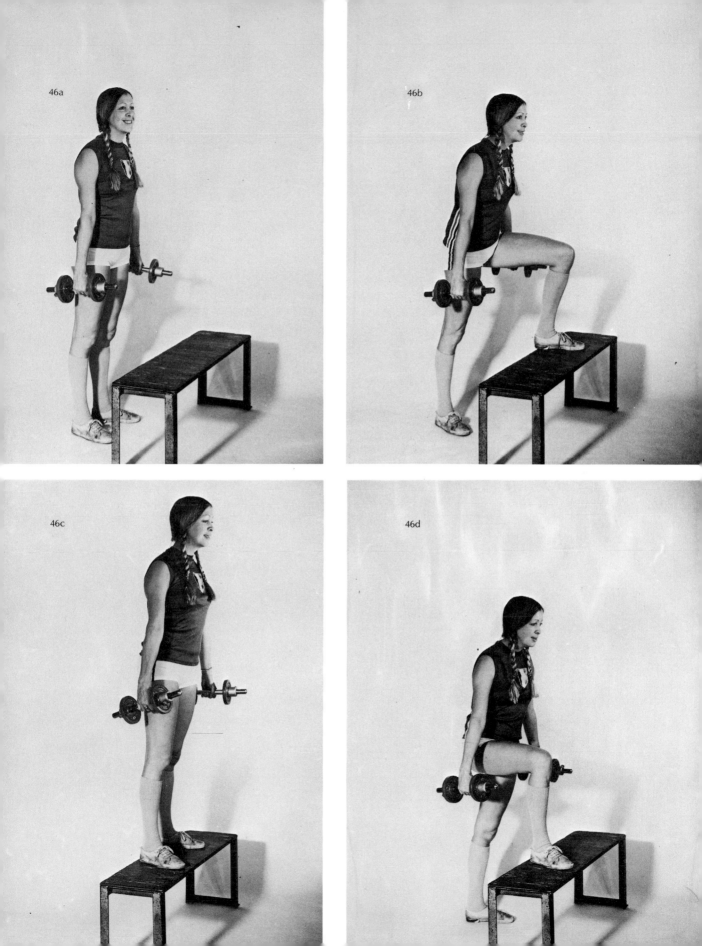

46a 46b 46c 46d

47 Vertical jumps.

47a

47b

repetitions. Hold a dumb-bell in each hand, keeping your arms hanging straight by your sides, and perform standing vertical jumps on the spot. Take care to absorb the shock of landing by bending your knees slightly and, at the same time, move downwards into a half squat position ready for the next jump. Jump as high as possible and keep your arms straight all the while.

Side Bends These are good for exercising your oblique abdominal muscles and also for mobilizing your trunk in the sideways direction. Hold a dumb-bell in one hand only by the side and bend as far as possible to each side in turn, without leaning forwards or backwards. Change the dumb-bell to the other hand halfway through the set.

48 Side bends.

48a

48b

49a

49b

49 The lateral raise.

Lateral Raise with Dumb-bells From the standing upright position with your arms by your sides and a dumb-bell in each hand, raise your arms sideways, without bending your elbows, until the dumb-bells are at shoulder level.

Frontal Raise with Dumb-bells This is similar to the lateral raise, except that the dumb-bells are raised forwards in front of the body.

Both lateral and frontal raises are useful for shoulder and back muscles.

50 The frontal raise.

51a 51b

51 The triceps curl.

The Triceps Curl This is a useful exercise for isolating the action of the triceps. It can be performed with one arm at a time or with both together. Hold a dumb-bell with your arm straight above your head and then slowly allow your elbow to bend without changing the position of your upper arm, so that the weight is lowered behind your neck.

Miscellaneous Exercises

Twisting with disc weight The muscles which act to produce trunk twisting movements are not well catered for in the weight trainer's repertoire, but there is one very good activity for gaining both strength and mobility in this respect – hold a disc weight (try about 5 kg at the start) in both hands and swing it horizontally round from side to side of your body. Balance will be difficult at first, so spread your feet wide and bend your knees slightly. Start the swing from the extreme position at the side with a rapid acceleration but slow the movement as the disc approaches the opposite extreme and allow the stretching with only a little momentum.

52 Trunk twisting with disc weight.

52a 52b

53 Vertical swing.

The movement can be confined to your trunk by keeping both elbows straight and your feet firmly in place on the floor.

Vertical Swing The vertical swing consists of a straight two-arm swing from the floor between the legs to directly overhead, and the weight (try about 5 kg at the beginning) can be a disc, a dumb-bell, a swingbell (a short bar, with disc weights at the centre, which is held by gripping on either side of the discs), or any suitable secure and compact object. Spread your feet slightly more than shoulder width apart directly over the weight, which you should grasp with both hands. Your legs should be bent and your trunk leaning only slightly more forward than in the normal squatting exercise. The weight is now lifted smoothly in a wide swinging movement forwards and upwards with your whole body until it arrives overhead on straight arms. Control the swing downwards again by counterbalancing with a slight backward shift of your bodyweight on to the heels.

54a 54b

54 The wrist roller.

The little skill involved in timing the swing properly for maximum effect can be learned quickly, making this lift a most enjoyable exercise for almost the whole musculature. It can also be used for deep breathing – breathe in on the upswing and out on the downswing.

The Wrist Roller Since the hands and wrists are involved in almost every weight training lift, it is not normally necessary to include specific work for the wrists in a schedule. Those with particularly weak wrists, or those recovering from injury may, however, find the wrist roller useful. This is a simple piece of apparatus which can be made up from a weight (start with 2½ kg) suspended on a 1·5 m length of thick string or light rope from the

middle of a dumb-bell bar or short length of broomstick. Hold the bar by over-gripping on either side of the rope knot. Stretch out to full arm's length horizontally in front, and, with a wrist action, roll the rope up around the bar, until the weight is raised to meet the bar. Now unroll the rope until the weight touches the floor again. As this wrist rolling is quite hard work on the forearm muscles, you will find that only a few repetitions are possible when you first try it.

Seated Wrist Curl Once again this exercise is superfluous to the needs of the normal weight trainer, and should only be used where the wrists are particularly weak. Use a barbell or set of dumb-bells and isolate the curling

55 The seated wrist curl.

55a 55b

56a 56b

56 Running arm action.

action to your wrists by sitting on a bench and leaning forward to support your forearms on your thighs.

Running Arm Action Many runners obtain useful specific upper body strength and endurance by practising a running arm action while holding a light weight in each hand. A stationary balance is maintained by putting one foot in front of the other and bending the knees slightly.

The Neider Press Bill Neider, a world record holder of the shot in the 1960s, designed an exercise specifically for the shot putting action. It is a fast front press with a modification – the barbell is pushed out and

upwards at an angle of about 45°. The starting position is similar to the front press except that the left foot is placed ahead of the right (vice versa for a left hander). As the lift is performed the right foot is allowed to make a step forward so that the lower body follows the barbell.

Exercises with Simple Apparatus

Some excellent exercises require only very simple pieces of apparatus, which, if necessary, can be improvised quite easily.

Abdominal Raise The abdominal raise (or abdominal curl) requires an inclined board on which you can lie full length with some

57 The abdominal raise with the hands behind the head.

57a 57b

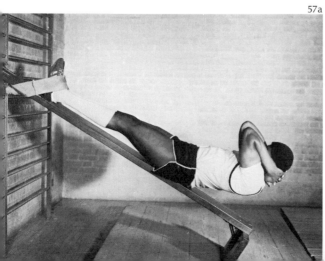

58a

58b

58 The slightly easier abdominal raise made with the hands at the sides.

means of securing your feet at the higher end. Your hands are clasped together behind your head (though beginners are advised to keep their hands by their sides for the first few weeks of training), and your upper body is raised until it is vertical, followed by a controlled lowering back into the lying position. Progression is obtained by increasing the angle of the incline and/or holding a disc weight behind your neck. Try using the abdominal raise as a deep breathing exercise by breathing out during the upward movement and breathing in while going back into the lying position.

Variations
1. A few more muscles of the trunk can be involved by adding a quick twist of your upper body at the top of the abdominal raise so that one elbow reaches towards the opposite knee. Alternate the direction of the twist with each repetition.
2. The abdominal raise can be performed with slightly bent knees or a stretching function can also be included in the exercise if your head is pushed as far as possible towards straight knees.
3. If an inclined board or bench is not available some useful abdominal work can be

59 The abdominal raise performed on the floor.

59a

59b

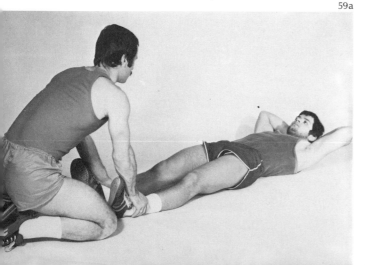

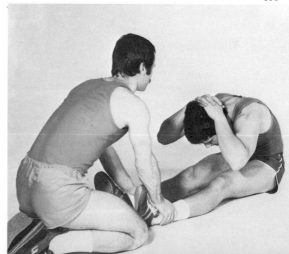

60a

60b

60c

60d

60 The abdominal raise with a trunk twist.

achieved by performing the abdominal raise on the floor with your feet secured under a barbell or any stabilizing object. The movement is very much easier than that on the inclined board, so a disc weight behind the head can increase the resistance, or a suitably large number of repetitions can be performed.

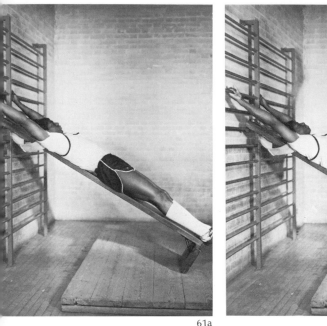

61a   61b   61c

61 The leg raise.

The Leg Raise The leg raise shifts the emphasis to slightly different abdominal and upper leg muscles, and is a reversal of the abdominal raise. Your head is at the higher end of the inclined board, and your upper body is secured by holding on to the board with your hands. You then raise your legs as high as possible overhead. If a wall rack is used to support the board, your hands may hold on to the rack as your feet are raised to touch the wall overhead.

The Abdominal Sit-up The sit-up on a bench is similar in some ways to the abdominal raise on the inclined board. Sit normally on a bench or stool with your feet hooked under a heavy barbell, and lean back as far as possible, holding your hands clasped behind your head. Now raise your upper body back into the sitting position. Carry a disc weight behind your neck to increase the resistance, if necessary.

Chinning on a Horizontal Bar Chinning requires a strong metal bar secured horizontally about 2½ m above the floor, so that you can hang full length by your hands without your feet touching the floor. For the best handgrip a bar diameter of 2½ cm is about right, so the ideal equipment is a gymnastics horizontal bar, or an old weightlifting bar fixed across the corner walls of a room. Stand on a chair placed slightly to the side of the bar, and take an undergrip with the hands slightly less than shoulder-width apart. Step off the chair, hanging full arm's length from the bar before commencing a pull upwards with your arms until your chin just touches the bar. Lower again until your arms are straight before starting the next repetition. This can be a difficult exercise at the beginning and there is a tendency not to lower down to full arm's length, but try to avoid this tenseness.

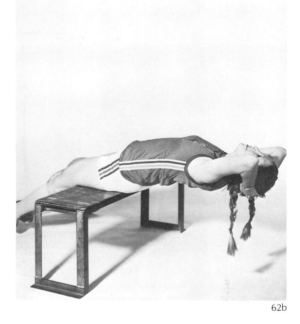

62a

62b

62 The abdominal sit-up on a bench.
63 Chinning the bar.

63a

63b

64 Chinning the bar with feet supported.

It must be pointed out that chinning to the bar is very difficult for women, most of whom may not be able to perform even one repetition. There are modified inclined chinning exercises for women in which some of the bodyweight is supported by the feet staying in contact with the floor, but these are not very effective. If you have difficulty with normal chinning it is better to work on barbell curls for these muscle groups.

Variations

1. The normal undergrasp chinning exercise may be varied by using *wide* or *narrow hand spacings*. If the movement becomes too easy

as strength is gained, it may be necessary to tie disc weights around the waist to increase the resistance.

2. *The over-grip chinning* exercise is for most people slightly more difficult, but is a useful variation. It is exactly the same as normal chinning except that an over-grip is used.

Pull-up Behind the Neck The chinning bar pull-up to behind the neck is not quite to be classed as a variation of chinning. It is an excellent exercise for the upper back and shoulder muscles, requiring a wide over-grip for the pull-up to the bar, the head dipping

65 Over-grip chinning.

66a

66b

66 Pull-up behind the neck.

forwards so that the top of the lift occurs as the back of the neck touches the bar.

Leg Raise on Horizontal Bar These are best done on gymnasium wall bars, but the chinning bar is a good substitute. While hanging with your arms straight throughout from an over-grip, lift your legs upwards by bending them at the waist. There are several variations which may be used as a progression as you become stronger.
Variations
1. *The bent leg raise* is quite easy and allows

your knees to bend as your thighs are brought up to the horizontal.
2. *The straight leg raise* involves more effort because your feet have to be lifted to waist level without bending your knees.
3. *The straight leg circle* is an advanced exercise in which your feet trace out a large vertical circle. Keep your elbows and knees straight all the while and move your feet out and upwards to one side, bringing them above your head and down the other side. On the next repetition reverse the direction of the rotation.

67 The bent leg raise.

68 The straight leg circle.

69a

69b

69 Dips on parallel bars.

Dips Parallel bars are necessary for dips. The body is supported by the arms at the sides and the exercise is simply a dipping of the body until there is a right angle at the elbows, followed by an extension of the arms to lift the body back to the starting position.

If parallel bars are not available a good improvisation is possible with benches or chairs. Two chairs support your arms so that your upper body can be dipped between them and your feet are supported on the third, so placed that most of the bodyweight is taken on the arms.

70 Dips with feet supported.

70a

70b

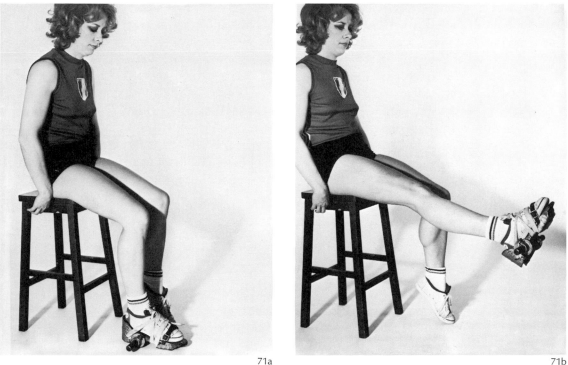

71a   71b

71 A leg extension with a weighted shoe. Disc weights may be added to the short bar.

Dipping on parallel bars is a particularly difficult exercise for women, but the proportion of bodyweight lifted by the arms can be reduced if the dipping is done between two chairs, as above, with the feet resting on the floor in front.

Weighted Shoe Exercises The so-called weighted shoe or boot, which is a metal frame with leather straps capable of holding a dumb-bell securely on the foot, is also used in remedial work. It provides variable loads for many different leg movements such as the seated leg extension (lifting the foot plus weight to a straight knee while seated), and the leg curl (flexing the knee from a face-down lying position), etc.

Neck Exercises with Head Harness Although the neck muscles are well exercised in many of the weight training exercises already mentioned, specific attention can be given to these muscles by using a harness which allows a weight to hang from your head to provide resistance to various movements.

Exercises with Special Equipment
In recent years the increasing popularity of weight training and growing awareness of the need for regular exercise has drawn the attention of inventors and manufacturers, with the result that a bewildering array of machines and gadgets are advertised for sale, many of them for home use. In general many of the pieces of apparatus and courses

73

advertised in magazines 'to give you a beautiful body in only six weeks' are a waste of money, because they simply become boring to use after a few sessions, and once the motivation and interest have gone, it is only a short time before that apparatus ends up forgotten in the cupboard. The more complicated the machinery, the greater is the likelihood that it will not be repaired when it inevitably breaks down. Unless dozens and dozens of different machines are available, the variations of exercises are limited, since they do not have the flexibility of the simple barbell. In any case, the strength athletes, like throwers, prefer the dynamic movements possible with heavy barbells.

On the other hand some useful and reliable weight training machines can be found in some of the more reputable gymnasiums. Several excellent multi-station machines are on the market, and although they are very expensive, they can produce good results if used sensibly. Some specialized machines have cams, instead of pulleys, designed to

72 An eight station Multigymn (centre) in use. Two other special purpose machines are shown at the sides (Photograph by courtesy of Powersport International Ltd.).

73a

73b

73 A leg curl machine.

ensure that the muscles experience optimum resistance throughout the range of the movement. Since these machines vary in design, it is not possible to give here a comprehensive list of exercises that can be performed on them, though many are similar in action to those used in normal weight training with barbells.

74 A leg press machine.

74a

74b

Exercises with Springs and Similar Devices

Before the advent of the machines, the main rival to the normal weight training barbell was the chest expander spring device, which still has its devotees. The apparatus consists of detachable steel springs, or thick elastic bands, of varying poundages and lengths, connected between two handles. Exercises can be performed by holding a handle in each hand and pulling them in opposite directions, in front of the body, behind the neck, etc. One handle can be attached to a wall or held down by a foot while you pull at various angles on the other handle. The force in the springs increases with extension, and

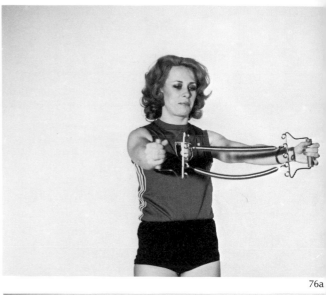

76a

76b

Above 76 Straight arm pull in front.

this can be both an advantage and a disadvantage depending on the exercise, since weak ranges occur at different stages in different exercises. The steel spring or rubber strand exerciser is light and easily portable, but on the other hand it takes some getting used to and its possibilities are limited.

Below 75 A chest-expander or steel spring puller. Between one and five springs may be used between the handles of this particular expander.

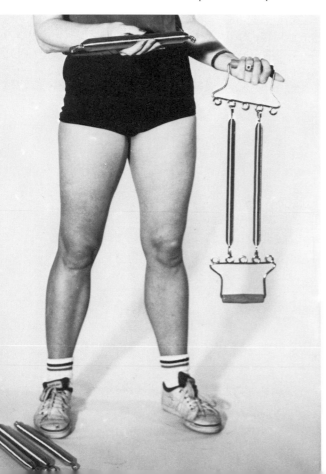

There are many spring-loaded devices available which have been designed in an attempt to increase the variations of exercises possible with ordinary chest expander springs. For example, some of these consist of metal tubes telescoping into each other against coil springs. With cords connecting the ends of the tubes, both pulling and pushing movements are possible.

Isometric Apparatus

An isometric contraction of a muscle occurs when there is no shortening of the distance between the muscle insertions – that is the contraction does not cause the load to move. In the early 1960s there was an isometric training craze, when it was shown that patients convalescing after illness made very large and rapid gains in strength through performing isometric exercises for only short periods each day. Although later a certain amount of doubt was raised about the effectiveness of this type of training for sportsmen, some people still play it safe and include isometrics in their schedules. In any case, when other forms of weight training are not available, one can improvise isometric exercises – pushing against walls, door lintels, desks etc. – which are better than no training at all.

Isometric apparatus comes in many forms, generally allowing one to push or pull against an immovable load which can be set at various positions through the whole range of the possible movement. For example, one version consists of two bars connected by a variable length of chain. The trainer stands on one bar and pushes or pulls against the other. The main objection to simple isometric apparatus is that motivation is lacking because the athlete doesn't know how much force he or she is exerting. This has been

77 An isometric apparatus which indicates the force exerted on the bar.

overcome in more sophisticated apparatus by including some form of indicator.

An isometric exercise consists of a maximum contraction for about five or six seconds, resting for about a minute, performing another maximum contraction for the same time with the apparatus adjusted to a slightly different position, resting again for a minute, and so on, with the contractions

77

78a 78b

78 A dynamic tension biceps curl.

repeated in various positions throughout the range of the movement. If an indicator of the force produced is available, it is a good idea to record the maximum readings at each setting, which can then act as motivation at the next training session.

Dynamic Tension

In the 1920s Charles Atlas and his partner, Dr Frederick Tilney, developed a body building course which included their own version of isometric exercising called 'dynamic tension'. This involved moving one part of the body while resisting with another part, for example, a one hand curl opposed by the other hand. The muscle contractions are virtually isometric because of the very slow movement. Objections to this type of exercise were based on the conflict produced in the mind when two parts of the body try to oppose each other. Certainly, effective dynamic tension requires a great effort of will.

Eccentric Training

The force developed in a muscle which is trying to contract, while being extended by a load too great for it to shorten, can be greater than the forces exerted in normal movement when loads are light enough for shortening of the muscle to occur. This type of muscle activity in opposition to the enforced movement is known as eccentric work. Since the energy produced in the muscle doesn't appear in the weight, except as a slowing down of its fall, this is sometimes called negative work. However, the results in terms of effect on the muscles are far from negative, and many weight trainers find that eccentric-type exercises can help them through certain sticking points in their conditioning programme. Since the forces in the muscles are larger than in concentric training, the conditioning of the muscles is correspondingly higher.

Eccentric training requires one, or preferably two, assistants who help raise the barbell to the top of the lift, where they allow the weight to fall against the athlete's resistance. The assistants grip the barbell again at the bottom of the lift and raise it for the next repetition. The problem of obtaining the services of two assistants can be solved if the assistants themselves are working on the same schedule, in which case they take turns at the exercise.

Eccentric training requires very heavy weights, so it should not be performed by anyone unless he or she has had many months of regular weight training immediately before the eccentric work period. Squatting with this method should only be undertaken in a rack, or in a situation where a stop is available to prevent the barbell sinking beyond the full squatting position of the athlete, if the assistants are unable to catch the bar at the right time. Also, because of the extremely concentrated effort required, repetitions should not be higher than about three. Rests between sets should allow complete recovery.

5 Getting Down to It

The Warm-up

The warm-up is that period of twenty to thirty minutes which prepares an athlete for the hard work of the session by means of gentle stretching exercises, light callisthenics, jogging and easy weights exercises. The warm-up before a weight training session is so important for the prevention of injuries that it is given a special section here.

A few research articles have been published which question the necessity of a warm-up before sporting activity, showing that groups of sportsmen training with and without a warm-up have had insignificant differences in their performances. No evidence of injury appeared in the non-warm-up groups. However this research has been confined to short periods of time, and has been carried out in temperate climates. No serious athlete starts on a session of hard weight training without some form of warm-up, even if the warm-up consists of easy movements with light weights. The fact that very little increase in deep body temperature occurs means that the name may be misleading, but this does not invalidate the effects.

Physiologically the warm-up stretches the muscles and tendons, decreases their viscosity and ensures an extra blood supply for the exertions to follow. Psychologically the warm-up provides a period of gentle transition from the sportsman's state of rest to one in which he or she must use much mental willpower and determination. The movements involved can also act as a mental rehearsal for those to come in the actual training session.

You will probably work out your own favourite warm-up routine, but to get you started you may try the following:
1. 800 m (half a mile) gentle jog, followed by
2. Ten minutes of yoga-type stretching exercises (avoid bouncing movements when approaching the extended position of a joint – rather relax so that the muscles and tendons are fully stretched), followed by
3. A few minutes of easy, free-swinging exercises (callisthenics), followed by
4. Two sets of power snatches, or high pulls with only 10 or 15 kg (20 or 30 lb) on the barbell.

Having warmed up doesn't mean that you should immediately start lifting your maximum poundages – on each exercise it is wise to include a preliminary set or two at poundages you can handle fairly easily. In other words, go through a mini warm-up on each exercise.

The Warm-down

It is a good idea to follow the example of many top-class athletes, and go through some of the above exercises at the end of a training session, since they will help to clear the musculature of the waste products of the heavy work, and there will be less chance of muscle stiffness the next day.

Schedules and Programmes

Beginner's Course It is important for the beginner to be patient and accept the fact that a gradual introduction to weight training is the best way of obtaining maximum satisfaction from the training in the long term. Poundages in the first week or two should be light, even apparently ridiculously light, to ensure that movements are learned correctly and that aching, stiff muscles don't result the day after training. It is advisable to start with a fairly general schedule which exercises the whole body, even though, for reasons to do with your sport, you may be wanting to strengthen one particular muscle group. It is better to carry out the basic course before starting on specific strengthening courses, since this will ensure that all the supporting muscle groups are well prepared.

Two sets of about ten repetitions on each exercise are adequate for a beginner in the first weeks, perhaps moving on to three sets of ten repetitions after this period. Include just two sessions a week in the first few weeks, then increase to three times a week if possible. As you gain strength and confidence, so your poundages can be increased and extra exercises and sets added. An excellent beginner's programme is as follows:

Week One (two sessions)
Power snatch – 15 kg (30 lb) × ten repetitions × two sets.
Press behind the neck – ditto.
Curl – ditto.

Squat – 20 kg (40 lb) × ten repetitions × two sets.
Bench press – 20 kg (40 lb) × ten repetitions × two sets.
Abdominal raise on gentle incline – bodyweight × ten repetitions × two sets.

Week Two (two sessions)
As for Week One but increase all weights (except for abdominal raise) by 5 kg (10 lb), and include after squats:
Bent arm pull-over – bar only × fifteen repetitions × two sets.

Week Three (three sessions)
As for Week Two but where possible increase all weights by another 5 kg (10 lb). If an exercise feels difficult with your present poundage, just stick to the same poundage on that particular exercise. Try to arrange time for a third session during the week.

Week Four (three sessions)
As for Week Three but, if the exercise feels easy, increase poundages as follows:
5 kg (10 lb) on power snatch, press behind the neck, curl and bent arm pull-over.
10 kg (20 lb) on squat and bench press.
Include at the end of the schedule:
Vertical jumps – 5 kg (10 lb) dumb-bells in each hand × fifteen repetitions × one set.

Week Five to Week Eight
If you have managed to keep to the programme for the first four weeks as above, you may enjoy changing to schedules which include many more exercises. Each session during the week contains a different schedule, the aim being to provide training for almost every muscle in the body, and to retain the novelty and interest in the programme. Poundages by now will be varying from person to person, so patience is required if

you find you are lagging behind on some of the exercises.

Day One

Power snatch – 20 kg (40 lb) to 30 kg (60 lb) × ten repetitions × three sets.

Press behind the neck – 15 kg (30 lb) to 30 kg (60 lb) × ten repetitions × three sets.

Curl – 15 kg (30 lb) to 30 kg (60 lb) × ten repetitions × three sets.

Front squat – build up from 20 kg (40 lb) × ten repetitions × three sets.

Flying exercise – 5 kg (10 lb) in each hand × ten repetitions × three sets.

Abdominal raise – 5 kg (10 lb) disc held behind neck × fifteen repetitions × two sets.

Side bends – from 5 kg (10 lb) dumb-bell × ten repetitions each side × two sets.

Bent arm pull-over – bar only × fifteen repetitions × two sets.

Day Two

Power clean – from 30 kg (60 lb) × ten repetitions × three sets.

Front press – from 20 kg (40 lb) × ten repetitions × three sets.

Reverse curl – from 15 kg (30 lb) × ten repetitions × three sets.

Squat – from 30 kg (60 lb) to 50 kg (110 lb) × ten repetitions × three sets.

Dips on parallel bars – ten repetitions × two sets.

Reverse abdominals – ten repetitions × two sets.

Upright rowing – from 15 kg (30 lb) × ten repetitions × two sets.

Vertical jump – 7 ½ kg (15 lb) on each dumb-bell × fifteen repetitions × one set.

Day Three

Split snatch – from 15 kg (30 lb) × ten repetitions × three sets.

Dumb-bell press – from 5 kg (10 lb) in each hand × ten repetitions × three sets.

Chin on horizontal bar – up to ten repetitions × two sets (long rest in between sets).

High pull – from 40 kg (80 lb) × ten repetitions × three sets.

Bench press – from 30 kg (60 lb) × ten repetitions × three sets.

Bent-over rowing – from 15 kg (30 lb) × ten repetitions × three sets.

Abdominal raise – no weight, one set to exhaustion. (This will be about twenty-five to forty repetitions.)

Week Nine

By this time you should be feeling stronger and quite confident at handling weights, so, if you wish, you can use Week Nine to try out your single-repetition maxima on certain exercises. Don't try all the maximum efforts on one day, but spread them over several sessions, so that you can include some normal exercise sets in each session as well. With assistants standing by, work up gradually in 5 kg (10 lb) increments until you can just manage one repetition on the following: front press, squat, bench press, power clean and power snatch. Not all exercises lend themselves to maximum poundages, so there is no point in attempting single-repetition maxima on such movements as abdominal raise and rowing.

Record the results of your testing in your training diary.

Weeks Ten, Eleven and Twelve

Using the results of the single-repetition maxima trials in Week Nine, adjust your schedule each session so that you work through a pyramid of sets (see Chapter 3) on one or two of these exercises. This will be a period of experimentation, and you will have to decide for yourself the starting poundages, the increments and the number of repetitions per set. When you strike the correct balance you should find that the last few repetitions of each set are quite difficult. If they are too easy, or if you cannot complete the set, adjustments are called for.

The other non-pyramid exercises in the programme should be worked in as before, with poundages being increased if their performance feels too easy.

At the end of the twelve weeks you should be feeling the benefits of your weight training efforts, and your improved physical condition should be helping your sport generally. As a weight training sportsman or sportswoman you will have graduated from the ranks of the beginners!

Advanced and Specific Training Schedules
The beginners' course lasting twelve weeks or so, described above, is designed to produce general over-all strength and some muscular endurance conditioning, and, with a few modifications, is suitable for people in many sports as an on-going programme of weight training. Some sports, however, place the strength emphasis on certain parts of the body more than on others – for example, swimming, gymnastics and canoeing require much muscular development in the upper body. On the other hand sports like middle and long distance running really demand their training to be biased towards the muscular endurance type of programme. Whichever training method is adopted it should be remembered that individuals will vary and participants in the same sport may require different exercises and programmes. So the construction of an advanced training schedule may need some thought which takes into account all of these factors.

Examples of Outline Programmes
Athletic throws The throwers in athletics come very close to Olympic weightlifters in their strength requirements, and should emphasize work on leg and back muscles – for example, with many low-repetition high-poundage sets of power snatches, power cleans, squats, dead lifts and high pulls. Bench presses of all types and dumb-bell flying exercises are necessary for shot putters and discus throwers, who should try for movements similar to the arm action in their throwing deliveries. Javelin throwers can imitate their arm action with pulley machines, and also by throwing iron balls slightly heavier than their javelins. Hammer throwers can add heavy hammer throwing to their weights programmes.

Athletic jumps The obvious exercises for long, triple and high jumpers are squats, vertical jumps with dumb-bells and split snatches – plus depth jumps without weights (jumping down from a bench to the floor followed by an immediate rebound jump on to another bench, etc.) Weights should be moved fast, so poundages need to be adjusted accordingly.

Running There is a whole continuum of schedules for runners ranging from the fairly low-repetition, fairly-high-poundage general spread of exercises of the sprinter to the high-repetition low-poundage leg and arm work of the long distance runner. The sprinter should do a lot more weight training than the long distance runner, who may only drop into the weights gymnasium once or twice a week for half-hour sessions.

Gymnastics Gymnasts have built-in weight training in their sport, since they are manipulating their own bodyweights most of the time. However, beginners may find their gymnastics limited if they cannot lift their own bodyweights in a press-up to a

83

handstand, for example, and they may find it helpful to turn to weight training with its gradual and progressive resistance possibilities.

Swimming Swimmers are divided over the effectiveness of weight training for their sport, and there have been world champions who have succeeded with and without it. The highly successful East-German swimmers spend 20 per cent of their training time at weights. Swimming is a very special sport in which the bodyweight is supported by the water, so that exercises like squatting will have very little effect on swimming performance except in starts and turns. Weight training exercises specific to the movements in swimming are difficult to achieve with ordinary weights, and one has to use awkward pulley arrangements to imitate the actions of the arms in the water. Some swimmers attempt to increase the water resistance to their arm movements by wearing hand paddles.

Whether or not weight training is beneficial to swimmers, if we at least accept that it is not detrimental to performance, it does provide a welcome break from the routine of the pool sessions.

Canoeing Unlike swimmers, canoeists are mostly convinced that weight training is an essential part of their conditioning. High-repetition bent-over rowing, bench pressing and abdominal exercises are particularly useful.

Rowing, judo, wrestling and rugby These strength sports involve the muscles of the whole body and demand the use of many different exercises in the weight training programme.

Tennis, squash and badminton In addition to a general weight training programme, sportsmen and sportswomen in the racket games can add the specific arm-strengthening exercises of lateral and frontal dumb-bell raises. Tennis, in particular, requires a strong arm to handle the heavy racket, and the unsightly thickening of the dominant arm can be modified by the use of weights.

Golf It may seem surprising to suggest that golfers can benefit from weight training, and yet many top-class professionals regularly use general weights exercises. The drive from the tee will be your measure of increased strength – but remember that strength and technique must be blended together, and that forcing a stroke will usually only lead to disaster!

Some golfers are convinced that strong wrists are the key to better swings, and continually squeeze away at squash balls or grip spring exercisers. There is no harm in these exercises, even though it is taking the idea of specificity to extremes, but quite often all that are needed in this particular respect are better designed rubber or leather grips on the clubs, or perhaps some resin on the hands.

Archery and shooting Again it may seem surprising to suggest that archers and shooters can improve their performances with weight training. Of course there will be considerable tremor for a short while after a weights session, but this disappears after a few hours, so no harm is done provided the weights don't immediately precede the shooting. Some exercises like dumb-bell lateral and frontal raises, bent-over rowing and upright rowing are fairly specific for the movements in these sports, but a general programme will also assist the demand on the postural muscles.

The above are only some random examples

of sports and the possibilities of improving performance in them through strength conditioning, but no one can deny the strength demands of sports like cycling, soccer, handball, volleyball, boxing, basketball etc. The sudden sprints involved in sports like cricket, fencing, lacrosse, netball and other team games require strong leg and back muscles – all amenable to weight training. Contrary to general belief there are considerable physical stresses on motor racing drivers, yachtsmen and riders, all of whom can benefit from a certain amount of weight training.

6 Other Applications

Circuit Training with Weights

Circuit training is a form of endurance conditioning in which various exercises are performed one after the other with no rest in between sets. The body is kept under considerable cardiovascular stress as strenuous work is performed for periods up to about twenty minutes. The name comes from the method of performing about a dozen exercises in a sequence of single high-repetition low-poundage sets, and then repeating the sequence two or three times in a circuit. A balanced circuit will include both free exercises, exercises with bodyweight and exercises with barbells and dumb-bells, but it is possible to devise circuits with weight training exercises only. Generally poundages are kept low, not only to ensure safety when fatigue sets in, but also to allow the work to continue aerobically, or, at most, just into the anaerobic state. Consecutive exercises can be similar if working aerobically, but they need to be different to allow recovery of the muscles concerned if they are heavy and produce oxygen debt. Obviously too much oxygen debt will lead to a breakdown in the circuit.

Numbers of repetitions per set are generally between ten and twenty depending upon the individual's state of fitness, and should be performed briskly and with good technique.

79 A push-up with feet raised.

79a

79b

80 A variation of the back hyperextension exercise.

Example of a Circuit (twenty to twenty-five minutes once or twice per week).

1. Step-up on bench (bodyweight only) – fifteen to thirty repetitions. Change leading leg in middle of set.
2. Bench press – 20 kg (40 lb) to 50 kg (110 lb) × ten to fifteen repetitions. (Alternative: Push-up.)
3. Abdominal raise on floor – ten to twenty repetitions.
4. Dips (bodyweight, or bodyweight partly supported) – eight to twelve repetitions.
5. Vertical jumps – 0–10 kg (20 lb) dumb-bells × ten to fifteen repetitions.
6. Rope climb – once up to 5 m (16 feet) and down.
7. Hopping – 10 m (30 ft) × four repetitions, alternating legs in each repetition.
8. Back hyperextensions – 0–10 kg (20 lb) × eight to fifteen repetitions. (Lie full stretch on stomach holding weight in front of head. Raise hands and feet from floor as far as they will go by arching the back.)
9. Chins – three to ten repetitions.
10. Power snatch – 20 kg (40 lb) to 40 kg (80 lb) × eight to twelve repetitions.
11. Side bends – 5 kg (10 lb) to 20 kg (40 lb) dumb-bell × ten to fifteen repetitions to each side.
12. Lateral raise – 2½ kg (5 lb) to 7½ kg (15 lb) dumb-bell in each hand × ten to fifteen repetitions.

Rest for one minute.
Repeat 1 to 12.
Rest for one minute.
Repeat 1 to 12 (if possible!).

Circuit training is a particularly useful method of conditioning for all team games during the pre-competition season, since it maintains match fitness. Participants in other sports with activities lasting more than a few minutes, for example the racket games, the combat sports, swimming and running, also have much to gain from including circuits within their training programmes.

The Disabled Sportsman or Sportswoman

Competitive weightlifting is already a well established sport for the blind or partially sighted, and paraplegics include the bench press in their competitions. Weight training is ideally suited to the disabled sportsman or sportswoman since a great deal of work can be done with little or no assistance. For example, as long as the paraplegic or leg amputee is safely secured, he, or she, can perform almost all the arm and upper body exercises. Wherever possible weights machines should be used since these generally ease the problems of deficient postural support muscles.

Similarly a temporarily disabled sportsman, with a broken leg for example, can maintain, and even gain, strength and tone in his uninjured muscles, by means of a modified weights schedule. The return to full sporting fitness will be much quicker than if no exercise is taken during convalescence.

Weight Training during Recovery from Illness or Injury

It is wise to be cautious about weight training during recovery from illness, and you should always seek advice from your doctor about when to resume, and the amount of work that should be attempted. Even for something as simple as a heavy cold or influenza it is advisable to rest for a few days and start up again very gradually. Obstinate determination not to miss a day's training in spite of illness will usually lower your body's resistance and lengthen the recovery period. However, when used properly and patiently without overstrain, weights can hasten your recovery to full fitness.

Similarly you should consult your doctor or physiotherapist about your training after injury. Merely to continue as before and 'train through the pain' can delay and even aggravate your injury. Physiotherapists use weight exercises regularly with their patients so they will be well qualified to advise you on your schedules.

If you have a minor injury which you are certain does not require a visit to the doctor or physiotherapist, make sure that you allow it plenty of opportunity to recover. Very light exercising will probably help, but use commonsense and don't load the barbell or dumb-bell to the point where pain is felt.

Remember that isometrics and dynamic tension can be of considerable help even when you are confined to bed, and indeed, you will relieve much of the tedium by thinking up and performing these exercises.

Gaining or Losing Bodyweight

Weight training can have several effects on bodyweight depending upon many factors such as your physical condition at the beginning, exercises used, poundages, numbers of repetitions, number of sets, frequency of sessions and diet during the training period. Of all these factors, you will find that diet is the most important, and that if you are trying to lose weight, no amount of exercise will have much effect unless it is combined with a sensible diet. One has only to look at paunchy super-heavyweight Olympic weightlifters, muscly body builders entering for Mr Universe competitions and elegant lady javelin throwers, all of whom use weights, to realize that weight training can be all things to all people.

Many people find that weight training stimulates their appetites, but although there is a consequent weight gain, it is smaller than if they had increased their food intake with no weight training, and the gain appears as firm muscle and not as fat. Of course excessive eating with weight training will lead to the type of fleshiness seen in some throwers who seem to think it necessary for their events.

Body builders have to work extremely hard and plan their diets carefully to produce the necessary muscle tissue adaptations and modifications. They are concerned mainly with sizes, shapes and proportions of muscles, and only to a lesser extent with strength and endurance, which they see as useful by-products to help them to increase the intensity of further training. Many critics of the body building fraternity see the diets they use as being gimmicky – fads to be exploited by the manufacturers of food supplements and vitamins. However, body builders do achieve remarkable results in altering the shape of their bodies, to the envy of both fat and thin people, so we do have something to learn from their methods.

While this book cannot go into the detailed physiology of weight gain and weight loss, it can state some commonsense facts. The human body is a remarkable machine in the way it controls its own weight. If you keep a daily check of your weight, you will find that it varies by about 1 kg (just over 2 lb) around an average which is quite resistant to attempts to alter it. However, there is a simple equation which applies to the energy requirements of the body. In this connection energy is measured in kilocalories (kcal) where 1 kcal is the energy required to raise the temperature of 1 kg of water by one degree Centigrade.

Total energy requirements = Basal energy requirements + Energy required for physical exercise.

The basal energy requirements are those necessary to support life, and vary between 1,500 kcal and 2,000 kcal per day according to age, sex, body build, climatic conditions etc. In addition, an active althlete will consume some 3,000 kcal per day, bringing his total up to around 5,000 kcal. Different activities require different amounts of energy – normal walking, for example, uses about 4 kcal per minute, whereas cross-country running uses about 10 kcal per minute.

All our energy requirements must be met by the intake of fuel in the form of food, water and air. In addition to providing fuel for energy, the food we eat must also contain material for building and repair of body tissues, and it must also supply the substances that act to regulate the body processes. For a detailed description of the various types of nutrients necessary for the body to function efficiently, the reader is advised to consult a good book on nutrition and diet. It is enough to say here that if the total calorie intake of the sportsman is greater than his total expenditure of energy, because he is overeating, his body will begin to convert the excess food into fat, and he will put on bodyweight. A poorly developed beginner at weight training in this situation will also put on bodyweight, but this will be due to the increase in muscle tissue resulting from the weight training. Conversely, if the total calorie intake of the sportsman is less than his total energy requirements, his body will begin to metabolize its fat deposits and he will lose bodyweight. Care must be taken in a programme of weight loss that the process is not taken too far, for eventually, when the fat stores are depleted, the body will begin to metabolize the protein in the muscles themselves, which will then deteriorate.

Any programme of weight gain or loss, to be successful without any ill effects, needs intelligence and patience. The bodyweight should be carefully monitored, preferably daily on an accurate set of weighing scales (bathroom scales are generally too inaccurate), and allowance must be made for a certain amount of normal fluctuation around the average. Keep a check on the fat deposits of the body – around the waist, on the back of the upper arms, around the neck etc. Patience is important because gains or losses should be slow and gradual – something like 1 kg (about 2 lb) a week at most. And remember all the while that the controlling factor is the food intake. There are all kinds of specialized diets and dieting fads, but we recommend that a good normal mixed diet of carbohydrates, fats, proteins, vitamins and minerals is adhered to, and that control is exercised in the total quantity eaten, rather than that one type should be excluded or supplemented. (For example, studies have shown that excess vitamins and minerals do not improve sporting performance.)

Drugs It is an unfortunate fact that some misguided weight trainers take various types of drugs either to increase their capacity for training or to alter their body chemistry, so that strength and/or bodyweight are increased rapidly and unnaturally. Many organizations controlling sport have rules banning drugs of this kind, but, in addition, the evidence is that these drugs are medically harmful – surely two good reasons for having nothing to do with them.

Conclusion – the Past, the Present and You

The history of a subject is usually written up at the beginning of a book, but as the history of weight training is so mixed up with that of weightlifting, it was decided that the weight training principles ought to be clearly defined before attempting to sort out the history of these activities. The ancient Greek sportsmen were probably the earliest recorded weight trainers, though their equipment was very unlike ours. They used small, hand-held weights for jumping and probably also in their running training. Surprisingly the principle of progressive resistance weight training is not a modern discovery – for as long ago as about 540 BC the Italian, Milo, improved his strength by carrying a calf on his shoulders for a while each day. As the calf grew, it became heavier and provided an increasing load for Milo, until eventually it was recorded that he carried the four-year-old heifer the full length of the stadium at Olympia. This is the equivalent of carrying 400 kg (900 lb) a distance of 180 m (600 feet). About thirty years ago Herbert Mann of Tennessee, USA, attempted to repeat Milo's training method and managed to reach the stage of carrying a 270 kg (600 lb) bull about the same distance. The experiment came to an end because the bull objected to this kind of treatment!

The relevance of Milo's training with the heifer is of particular interest to us because he was primarily a wrestler and not a showman weightlifter. He won six wrestling championships in the Olympic Games, and was such a certain winner of his seventh Games title that the event was cancelled because no one dared wrestle with him!

From about the seventeenth century onwards there was an ever-growing interest in feats of strength. It is suggested that the dumb-bell originated in England about this time, because a convenient way of constructing a weight was to fix two heavy bells, with the clappers removed, one at each end of a stick – hence 'dumb' bells. John Paugh in 1728 suggested that dumb-bells could be used in physical training, but the public imagination was fired by the travelling professional strongmen for the next 150 years, and it was not until the late nineteenth century that a German, Dr Frederick Jahn, established physical training programmes which included weight training with dumb-bells.

In 1902 Alan Calvert founded the Milo Bar-Bell Company in the USA, and began manufacturing plate-loading barbells for amateurs. He also published a magazine called *Strength* in which he demonstrated, in text and pictures, the benefits and pleasures to be derived from 'progressive' weightlifting.

In spite of the Depression and the World Wars, weight training steadily grew more popular, and after the Second World War it really became established as an important training aid to other sports. It has been a major factor in the athletics performance explosion of recent years, and top-class participants in other sports like squash, badminton, soccer and golf are leading the way for a similar awakening of interest in the benefits to be gained for their sports from weight training.

The acceptance of the importance of weight training for sport in the last thirty years or so started with the use of the good old barbell, and even today, with a multitude of machines and gadgets available, it is still the most used piece of equipment.

The progressive resistance exercises possible with weights allow adjustments for increasing gains in strength so that you are always training at your optimum level. The gains you make are evident as extra weight on the bar, and therefore act as a strong motivation to further training. The transfer of the benefits into your sport vary according to the nature of the sport – from the almost direct application for a shot putter, to the vague 'generally feeling physically better' carry-over for the team-games player. So, accordingly, some people will make more use of the weights gymnasium than others. But as has been argued in this book, even if weight training isn't going to make a tremendous improvement to a long distance swimmer's times, at least it can provide a useful break from work in the pool.

The old myths and fallacies of harmful effects of weight training for men have died, but in countries like Britain they still survive as far as weights for women are concerned. Our women will not be able to compete in many sports on equal terms with their counterparts in Eastern European countries until they come to regard weights as an essential part of their training.

You may find that weight training remains a part of your life even after you retire from active participation in your main sport, for long-term regular exercise is a necessity for healthy living. Weight training is one of the best and most convenient ways of achieving this regular exercise, even though as you grow older the poundages may need to be adjusted downwards a little.

One of the benefits of weight training lies not in the physical effects on the body, but in the mild self-discipline it imposes on you. If you can develop the kind of willpower and drive that requires you to heave weights around for half an hour three times per week, you aren't likely to be overcome by the stresses of modern living quite so easily.

There are many factors involved in weight training, not least of which is your body's own unique adaptation to it, so the effectiveness of the programmes you work through are very much a matter for careful observation on your part, followed by intelligent experimentation to discover the optimum training conditions for you. It is important that you should enjoy your training, if it is not to become drudgery. The challenge of discovering how to improve your own sporting performance will be most enjoyable. And in the process you will meet, in the gymnasium, others from different sports who are also seeking self-improvement. You are certain to gain from the new friendships you will make.

Good lifting!